LIVING AND DYING
ON A SHARED EARTH

This course is dedicated to the memory of Dr Richard Holmes, a Senior Lecturer in Biology (1971–1993) and former Pro-vice-chancellor for Student Affairs at the Open University. Richard's vision was an inspiration in laying the foundations for *Human Biology and Health*.

SK220 Book 5
A second level course

LIVING AND DYING
ON A SHARED EARTH

HUMAN
BIOLOGY
AND HEALTH

BOOK 5

Edited by Heather McLannahan

The SK220 Course Team

Course Team Chair
Michael Stewart

Course Manager
Verena Forster

Course Team Secretary
Dawn Partner

Academic Editors
Brian Goodwin (Book 1)
Michael Stewart (Books 2 and 3)
Jill Saffrey (Book 3)
Frederick Toates (Book 4)
Heather McLannahan (Book 5)

Authors
Janet Bunker (Books 1, 2 and 3)
Melanie Clements (Book 3)
Basiro Davey (Books 1 and 2)
Brian Goodwin (Book 1)
Linda Jones (Book 1)
Jeanne Katz (Book 5)
Heather McLannahan (Book 5)
Hilary MacQueen (Books 1 and 4)
Jill Saffrey (Book 3)
Moyra Sidell (Book 5)
Michael Stewart (Book 2)
Margaret Swithenby (Book 1)
Frederick Toates (Books 2, 3 and 4)

Editors
Andrew Bury
Sheila Dunleavy
Sue Glover
Gillian Riley
Margaret Swithenby

Design Group
Martin Brazier (Designer)
Sarah Hofton (Designer)
Steve Best (Graphic Artist)
Andrew Whitehead (Graphic Artist)

BBC
Sandra Budin
Rissa de la Paz
Phil Gauron
Paul Manners
Ian Thomas
Nick Watson

OU Course Consultant
Chris Inman

External Course Consultant
Bill Tuxworth (University of Birmingham)

External Course Assessor
Professor Jennifer Boore (University of Ulster)

First published 1997. Reprinted 2001.

Copyright © 1997 The Open University.

All rights reserved. No part of this publication may be reproduced, stored in a retrieval system or transmitted in any form or by any means, without written permission from the publisher or a licence from the Copyright Licensing Agency Limited. Details of such licences (for reprographic reproduction) may be obtained from the Copyright Licensing Agency Ltd, 90 Tottenham Court Road, London, W1P 0LP.

Edited, designed and typeset in the United Kingdom by the Open University.

Printed and bound in Singapore under supervision of MRM Graphics Ltd, Winslow, Bucks.

ISBN 0 7492 8156 1

This text forms part of an Open University Second Level Course. If you would like a copy of *Studying with The Open University*, please write to the Course Enquiries Data Service, P.O. Box 625, Dane Road, Milton Keynes, MK1 1TY, United Kingdom. If you have not enrolled on the Course and would like to buy this or other Open University material, please write to Open University Worldwide, The Berrill Building, Walton Hall, Milton Keynes, MK7 6AA, United Kingdom.

CONTENTS

CHAPTER 1
INTRODUCTION

This book has two aims. Firstly, we set out to confront some of the issues surrounding ageing and death. The second aim is to place human activities into a wider context, showing how our biology links with our surroundings. To accomplish this, we return to a theme raised at the beginning of the course, namely that the health of the individual should not be studied in isolation from their environment.

Each of these topics provides sufficient material for a course in its own right. This means that what we have to say here is necessarily fairly selective, even superficial. You will find that fewer demands are made of you and there are fewer bold terms, activities and questions.

Throughout the course we have tried to present health issues alongside the study of our biological natures. When we say that we have taken an holistic approach, we mean that we have tried to allow the lessons learned from one discipline, such as biology, to inform our understanding and study of phenomena at other levels, such as sociology and psychology. For example, we have not simply studied feeding and diet from the standpoint of biological processes such as digestion and assimilation of essential nutrients, but have widened the discussion to try to understand why people might eat differently in different situations and at different times in their lives. We have seen that what you choose to eat may depend on how much money you can spend on food, how many others are sharing food with you and what your relationship is to them, as well as such considerations as your age, health and physical condition.

The integration of these different aspects of feeding behaviour involves an understanding of homeostasis. The concept of homeostasis has been very important throughout the course. Each individual is in a state of dynamic balance both internally and within the wider framework of family and society. Life is only possible provided that certain variables are maintained within fairly restricted limits and we have studied both the physiological and psychological mechanisms that enable this homeostasis to be achieved. The course has emphasized that the study of human biology is not the study of a static system; there is constant change and development.

Development and developmental processes were very much to the fore in Book 1, and each subsequent book has returned to the theme of change and development. When we studied the respiratory and circulatory systems in Book 3 (Chapter 2), there was a reminder that change takes place during development and at birth. There was also considerable detail given about the changes that can occur in response to altered external conditions, such as going to live or work at high altitudes. However, the emphasis was on 'maintaining' the whole, which carries with it the idea that one can continue in some way *unchanged*, except for necessary adjustments in response to a changing environment. This view is not quite correct because there is another complicated aspect of human health and biology: the phenomenon of ageing.

Biological change means that we are in some sense never at a standstill. Ageing is not something that starts at a particular age. We are ageing throughout our lives; it is not only those designated 'elderly' who experience ageing. Although we operate with notions of 'young', 'middle-aged' and 'old' as though they were clear categories, if you asked ten people to give you their definition of these categories or to locate them on a chronological scale you would probably not get the same responses. Guessing someone's age can be a very difficult and sometimes sensitive issue. Although we are all ageing throughout the lifespan, we do not do so in a set, chronological way. Our lives are not set to run along some predetermined pathway; we are constantly changing in highly individual and different ways. Many of these changes are in response to external events. There is the example of the hormonal changes that occur during pregnancy where, after giving birth, the body does not simply revert to its pre-pregnant condition. One is truly never the same again! It is often not possible to distinguish between these kinds of exogenously generated changes and the endogenous changes that also take place. An arthritic joint in one person might be attributed to a memorable sports injury sustained many years previously; in another person there might seem to be no cause other than 'old age'. Yet, does anyone get through childhood without ever spraining an ankle or in other similar ways buffeting their body? Could it be that all the symptoms of old age have as their cause some unnoticed mistreatment of the body at an earlier age? Chapter 2 discusses aspects of growing older; it won't answer this question, but it will describe some of the commonly observed changes associated with ageing and their implications for our health and well-being.

These implications extend beyond the physical considerations of whether you can still perform necessary activities (e.g. is it *necessary* to be able to run to catch a bus?), to the psychological (e.g. how do you *feel* about not being able to run for the bus?), and the sociological (e.g. what are the social and functional implications if you can't run for the bus?). Although the chapter spends much time describing biological change, and the theories put forward to explain that change, it also looks at psychological and sociological explanations which try to understand human ageing. Similarly, explanations of health in old age are looked at from the different perspectives of biology, psychology and sociology. We hope that you will be able to keep the course theme of health in mind and continue to ask yourself how ideas of health change with age. This question was first posed in Book 1 (Chapter 2), and we use two case studies in Chapter 2 of this book to help you with this task. We also raise the currently topical question of how society is to cope with increasing numbers of older people who need resources beyond those that they can afford.

Chapter 3 is a little unusual for a course on human biology in that it describes the biological processes of death. Depending on your disposition, it is possible that you could find some of this disturbing. (I certainly found researching the material upsetting at times!) Death can occur at any age and there is a theory suggesting that all deaths are accidental. They do become more likely the longer we live and this is explained by the **disposable soma theory** of the evolution of ageing and death. This theory, which is discussed in Audio sequence 2 (see below), was proposed by Thomas Kirkwood when he was working for the Medical Research Council in Manchester. The theory is named after a Western economic phenomenon whereby manufactured articles are produced with a minimum investment in durability. Machines such as cars and washing machines are only built to last for a limited length of time. It would be possible, though more expensive, to make them last longer, but fashions change, new developments come along and the consumer is thought to prefer to invest less in machines and then dispose of them without any qualms. By analogy, it is suggested that organisms derive little benefit from investing resources in increasing their lifespan beyond a certain point. To invest in repairs and maintenance in the expectation of an infinite lifespan is inefficient, because the inevitability of eventual death through some kind of accident means that resources that could have been put into reproduction will have been wasted. Thus, the disposable soma theory argues that the optimal level of investment in the soma (soma means body) is less than would be required for the indefinite survival of the individual. It is because we are going to die at some point in time that we show the various manifestations of ageing. We have not been able to invest sufficient resources to prevent them from occurring.

Even if all deaths are accidents, we know that some occur suddenly and shockingly, at any age, whilst others become predictable, again at any age. The experience of dying and of death, both for the individual and for those who have been bereaved is unique. Some of you will have thought about the issues that we will be discussing in Chapter 3 in greater depth than we have found possible within such a short space. You may feel that we have left out or glossed over important aspects of your own or of other people's experiences. Others of you may not have had reason to think about these topics at all. Either way, we hope that if you feel a need to talk to others about material in this chapter you will find fellow students or your tutor to have a sympathetic and helpful approach.

In Chapter 4 we describe some of the ways in which all the components of our planet interact and show how dependent we are on the continuing health of the planet for our own health and survival. Unfortunately, many human activities lead to environmental changes which have negative consequences. Science cannot always predict the eventual outcome of these changes, and we use the phenomenon of global warming to illustrate this point. We can be left feeling powerless in the face of these large global issues; nevertheless, there is some scope for individual life choices.

Audio sequence 2 relates to material in Chapter 2 of this book. We recommend that you listen to the audio sequence before you begin your study of this chapter.

CHAPTER 2
GROWING OLDER

2.1 Introduction

Humanity as a whole is growing older. In 1900 it was estimated that just 1% (10–17 million people) of the global population was over the age of 65 years. By 1992, 6.2% (342 million people) of the total population was over 65. It is estimated that by 2050, 20% (2.5 billion people) of the total population will be over 65 (Olshansky *et al.*, 1993). In the economically developed world the proportion of older people is highest: 17% in the UK, with 13% or more in other parts of Europe. This trend is set to spread over the whole world as we move into the 21st century, as shown in Figure 2.1.

Increasing longevity is generally seen as a health gain. So, why do some people view an ageing population without enthusiasm? Instead of being a source of celebration we are bombarded with terms such as the 'burden of dependency' and 'a drain on our resources'. Why do most of us want to live a long life but few of us want to age? How do you view the prospect of old age?

The following quotes from ancient Roman writings represent the optimistic and pessimistic views, which are still prevalent today.

Seneca was optimistic:

> *Let us welcome old age and cherish it; if we know how to make the most of it, it is full of comforts. Fruit has its best flavour only when it is fully ripe. Gliding down the slope of the years with a motion that is not yet in any way abrupt or sudden is an exquisite time of life. (Quoted in de Beauvoir, S., 1977, p. 136.)*

The Elder Pliny was less enthusiastic:

> *The shortness of life is undoubtedly nature's blessing. The senses grow dull, the limbs stiff; sight, hearing, legs, teeth and even the organs of digestion move towards death faster than we. (Quoted in de Beauvoir, S., 1977, p. 136.)*

Let's get one tiresome question out of the way: when do we become old? This prompts many complicated questions which will pervade most of this chapter. Here we give a practical, chronological answer which is: when we reach the age beyond which most of us are no longer in paid employment. This is around 60–65 years. Gerontologists, who study the process of ageing, have recently split what is a very long period into two. They have introduced the notion of a third and fourth age or, young-old (60–74) and old-old (75+).

Whether we view the ageing of the population with joy and celebration, or alarm and dismay, depends to a great extent on the likely health status of that ageing population. In this chapter we will first look at the health implications

(a)

(b)

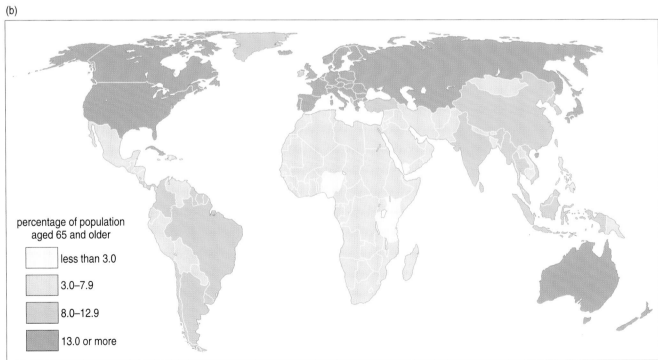

Figure 2.1   Ageing of the world population: (a) 1990 data; (b) projected data for 2025.

for populations before focusing on the implications for individual older people.
We will end with some predictions and choices that face humanity as it ages.

That human life is finite seems sure, but the potential length of human life is less sure, and longevity is a common measure of the health of populations. A great many resources, both human and economic, are brought to bear in increasing lifespan, especially in the economically developed world.

Most of us would now feel cheated by only three score years and ten, as the number of telegrams sent by the Queen to those reaching 100 increases year by year. Does this mean that more of us are reaching the full potential lifespan, so that in longevity terms the population is getting healthier? Alternatively, is the potential lifespan lengthening with the implication that health measured by mortality is a moving target. Further, if we are living longer is it worth it in terms of our health and well-being? If we measure health by the absence of disease or in terms of physical fitness or well-being, are the added years merely adding extra unhealthy years?

These issues have been hotly debated and the thesis put forward by Fries and Crapo (1981) on the **rectangularization of mortality**, has been very influential in this debate. Figure 2.2 represents their thesis graphically.

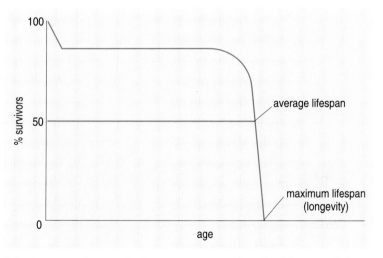

Figure 2.2   Rectangular survival curve, representing the lifespan of the population of modern Western societies.

The rectangularization of mortality thesis indicated in the diagram is based on the assumption that there is a *maximum* limit to the human lifespan of about 120 years. Fries argued that, as premature mortality decreases, more people reach the limits of this natural lifespan. Mortality increasingly occurs at the end of the lifespan giving this rectangular-shaped pattern. Death occurs as the body wears out rather than because of trauma or disease.

Some of the current theories of human ageing tend to support this view that life expectancy is unlikely to increase much beyond the present level. For example, there is a suggestion that certain human cells are internally programmed for only a limited number of divisions, although these views are not universally held. Most of the counter-evidence comes from biologists who have selectively bred strains of animals that have lifespans up to twice the length found in natural populations. Further support that human lifespans have considerable potential to increase comes from computer models, generated from the pattern of deaths of 4 000 Danish twins born between 1870 and 1890 (McGue *et al.*, 1993). These results suggest that if death occurs before 110 years of age it is 'premature'. Other scientists specializing in this area of study believe that an expectation of a 200-year human lifespan will be realized in the not too distant future. This would have huge resource implications, especially as another aspect of the Fries and Crapo thesis, the **compression of morbidity**, is also contentious. They argue that not only are more people reaching the natural limits of life but that disease and decay are put off until, or compressed into, the last few years of life when the body simply falls apart or wears out. This is known as **terminal drop**. Present empirical evidence does not support this optimistic scenario for the compression of morbidity.

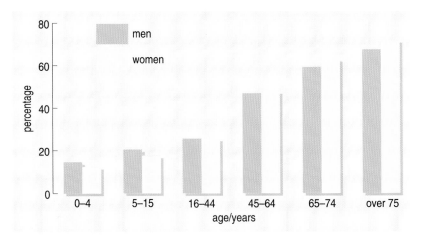

Figure 2.3   Percentage of people with long-standing illness in Great Britain, 1990.

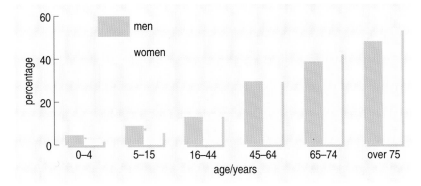

Figure 2.4   Percentage of people with functionally limiting long-standing illness in Great Britain, 1990.

Figures 2.3 and 2.4 (previous page) indicate that health, if measured by the absence of disease, i.e. the medical model (Book 1, Section 2.2.1), is poor for a great many older people. Around 60% of all older people suffer from some **chronic illness**. However, 40% of older people do not, so which older people are prone to chronic illness and disability in later life? If we break these overall figures down according to various **socio-economic categories** it is clear that certain categories have more than their fair share of illness in old age.

Table 2.1 Older respondents with a long-standing illness or disability. (*n* is the number of respondents.)

	Women over 65		Men over 65	
	$n = 2\ 090$ % yes*	Limits activity[†]	$n = 1\ 436$ % yes*	Limits activity[†]
all	60	73	56	71
age groups				
65–74	56	68	55	70
75–84	64	76	57	73
over 85 years	71	86	63	82
marital status				
married	55	72	52	86
single	57	72	52	86
widowed	64	74	59	73
social class				
non-manual	57	70	49	64
manual	63	76	59	76
housing classes rents from local authority	64	76	60	76
owner occupier	55	69	53	66
other rental	61	71	59	76
education some qualifications	44	58	52	65
no qualifications	57	66	58	73
self-assessed health good	31	45	33	44
fairly good	66	68	64	71
not good	92	90	90	91

* Percentage of respondents with a long-standing illness or disability.
[†] Percentage of 'yes' respondents whose activity is limited.

The table shows that a widowed working-class woman, living in local authority rented accommodation who has no educational qualifications, is much more likely to suffer from some form of chronic illness or disability than a well-educated married middle-class man, living in his own house. However, these figures only break down the older population into very broad categories. Health in later life varies a great deal and is the product of a whole lifetime's experience. What does ageing mean in human terms? What does it feel like?

The health experience of two women, Miss Hamish and Lily Bradshaw, in the following case studies, are very different. As you read them try to identify the different factors which might be contributing to their present state of health.

Lily

Lily lives in a one-bedroom modern bungalow in a charitable housing complex for older people. She is 74 years of age and, in common with many other older women, does not have just one chronic health problem, but three: bad legs due to varicose veins; arthritis in her right hip which she says is going across into her spine, and a Parkinson's tremor.

She has considerable pain from her arthritic hip, she cannot walk far and only manages to walk about the flat, although she goes out in the minibus occasionally. Her hands tremble and she has difficulty holding a cup of tea. She always lifts the cup and saucer together to try to prevent spillage on her clothes, but even so she is usually unsuccessful. This is a source of great embarrassment and means that she avoids most social occasions and only maintains contact with one or two very close friends and her family. But most of all she complains of tiredness; a constant feeling of wanting to lie down and rest.

I never want to do anything. All I want to do is lie on the bed, that's how I feel, that's being honest. It sounds lazy, but it's not laziness, I've just no energy. I feel as though my legs won't go.

She makes herself do one housework chore each day. She will hoover one day, change her sheets another and so on, but it always takes it out of her, as she says, 'all my get up and go is gone'. She is not aware of any family history of arthritis or Parkinson's disease although her mother had varicose veins. It is her firm belief that her present ill-health is all due to stress.

I think all of it is the stress of everything, I think it's come to sort of a climax now. I can't explain it. It's sort of come to a head and I think it's all the stresses have really wore me out, and I'm tired, really tired now. I've had so much stress in my life, I think that's what it's done to me. It's sort of drained me, I've nothing left. This trembling, I think stress has brought a lot of it. Stress can cause a lot of things, you've probably got it but it sort of brings it out. Stress is terrible for people.

Most of the stress to which she refers is due to a very unhappy marriage. This was made doubly stressful because of her lifetime's involvement in the church. The shame of a broken marriage was almost as bad as the marriage problems. Throughout the 30 years of their marriage, her husband had constant affairs which she tolerated because they had four children, and divorce was against her religious principles. In the end, when the children were grown up and he was living part of the week at home and part with his other woman, she insisted that he decide on one or the other and he chose to leave her. Lily described how she was left on her own and worked railway gates which gave her an income and a place to live. But it was hard work and she had to be up through the night and in all weathers.

In spite of all this misfortune she does her best to be cheerful:

> *I've always had a good laugh. I laugh at things, at some things I shouldn't. I'm not always cheerful. Sometimes I have a little weep, on the quiet, nobody ever sees it. I keep that to myself. I think it does you good to have a weep, it relieves you.*

She has pain-killers for the arthritis and some cream from the doctor and is resigned to her conditions:

> *You just accept them don't you. You don't sort of get over it do you? You don't get better, so you've just got to accept them, and do what is best for you as regards treatment or anything else. Like my arthritis, he gives me cream, I rub myself with cream and sit on a hot water bottle, I do all sorts.*

Miss Hamish

Miss Hamish is 89 years old, and very much a well person. She does all her own shopping, cooking and cleaning. She describes herself as:

> *...fit as a fiddle. I've always been one for sports, cycling and skating and swimming and gymnastics.*

She still walks a lot and swims once a week with an evening class. She has also attended woodwork and pottery classes.

Her hearing is not as good as it used to be and she has an NHS hearing aid. She also had a period of bad eyesight before her cataract was operated on and this limited her activities and was not a happy period for her. She is very pleased with the cataract operation because it has restored her confidence which failing eyesight had threatened. Recently she had a bad cold and so did not venture out as the weather was quite autumnal. She really found that very frustrating and says that she dreads becoming housebound.

Her only complaint at the moment is itchy skin which she says, 'drives her silly'. She has been prescribed creams by her GP who is very sympathetic and referred her to a skin specialist. However, the tests revealed nothing and it seems there is little that can be done. So she 'ladles' cream on to her skin and, as she says, at least it doesn't keep her awake at night.

Although her visits to the surgery are infrequent, she always goes immediately if she is worried about anything and feels that she receives good treatment; she has no complaint. She also regularly attends the chiropody clinic held at her local health centre and is very concerned to maintain her feet in good working order. In all, she seems to take very sensible precautions concerning health but does not engage in health-promoting activities for health's sake. Her swimming and other activities are primarily for recreation and are part of her accustomed lifestyle. For her, health is very much about being able to carry on with her usual activities, even though those activities may not be regarded by some as attainable at nearly 90. When asked to what she attributes her own good health, Miss Hamish refers to her Scottish upbringing:

> *Well, it sounds absurd but I wasn't brought up to make too much fuss of myself. Scottish people, they're well even if they can hardly crawl about.*

But her relationship to her parents she thinks was significant in other ways. They were devout Christians and in fact her father worked as secretary for a missionary society in Scotland. She describes her upbringing as narrow to a degree. Her parents were very caring but her mother was particularly domineering:

> *She sat on me, she was very overwhelming.*

As a young woman, Miss Hamish felt oppressed by her parents and needed to break away. This she did, she rejected them and their religion and this was like starting a new life. She describes herself as a strong person, but she felt stifled especially by her mother. Miss Hamish has a sister who is 91 and apart from some arthritis she is well. She has a brother in Devon who is 75 and apparently very well and her younger sister died at the age of 85. As she says, they have mostly outlived their parents, although her father lived till he was 80 and her mother died at 66.

She had been a schoolteacher all her life and had enjoyed working with children. She had never married due, she says euphemistically, to having been 'disappointed' when in her twenties. In any case she thinks she would probably have been too independent. She clearly takes control of her life and does not leave things to chance, i.e. she nurtures herself (Book 1, Chapter 2).

The health status of these two women is very different. In fact it is the much older Miss Hamish who is fitter and healthier. If you look back at Table 2.1 you will see that their socio-economic circumstances correspond to the categories of those with more or less chronic illness and disability. Lily was divorced and is now widowed, Miss Hamish is single. Miss Hamish is from the **non-manual class**, she has been an owner occupier and she is an educated woman. Lily is from the **manual class**, has had little formal education and has lived in rented accommodation for all her life. But you will note that neither attribute their good or poor health to any of these factors. Lily is convinced that the stress of her unhappy marriage and subsequent divorce is responsible for her ill-health. Miss Hamish puts her good health down to strength of character and being in control. Of course, some of these characteristics are not unrelated to social class and education but they do make the picture much more varied. So how can we begin to unravel some of these complex factors which affect health in old age? It is important to look for patterns and similarities as well as explore differences.

In the following sections we will first describe the physical patterns of ageing before going on to find out what we can learn from other perspectives such as the sociological and psychological.

Summary of Section 2.1

1   The world's population, especially in the Western world, is ageing. This has important implications for the health and well-being of not only older people but the population as a whole.

2   The health status of the current older generation is very varied. One's chronological age is not an adequate indicator of health. In statistical terms, health is clearly related to socio-economic variables. At the individual level, the accumulated effects of a long life as well as personal characteristics, both physical and psychological, all make for a very complex picture of health in old age.

2.2 Physical aspects of ageing

Ageing of course begins the moment we are born but we use different types of words to describe the processes at different ages.

Think of the words we use to describe ageing at different stages of life.

From birth until the age of 18 or 20 we talk of development because the young person's body is showing increased competence and chances of survival are continuing to improve. After 20 and up to 40 or perhaps 50 we talk of maturity. In fact, a retrograde change in some organs has already begun but, in general, we compensate quite efficiently for loss, deterioration and failure until at least our fifth decade. When deficiencies are not compensated for and the adult becomes more susceptible to damage and deterioration, then we begin to talk of decline. At each of these stages we recognize age difference but few of us would claim to be able to accurately identify another person's chronological age based on outward appearance. Ageing does not proceed in a linear fashion with clearly identified milestones. We each age at different rates, we start to age noticeably at different times and in different ways. Nor is this a steady progression of biologically driven events, as we ourselves acknowledge when we make remarks such as 'The pressure over these past two weeks has aged me by about 20 years!' and 'Her looks belie her age'. So how shall we define ageing?

Biologists who specialize in ageing have defined it as follows:

> ...a period in the lifespan that is characterized by an increased vulnerability and a decreased viability. There is a failure to maintain homeostasis during psychological stress. (Davies et al., 1994, p. 8)

Homeostasis is a term you have come across many times in this course. It embodies the idea that the body maintains a dynamic relationship with the external environment, enabling it to regulate its own internal environment around particular set-points. For example, it involves water and salt balance as well as temperature regulation. Old age is seen as a time when we cannot maintain normal body function effectively.

Why does this happen? Could we not keep our youthful looks and energy until the end? Is there any way we could maintain all our bodily parts and functions in 'tip top' working order? To answer this, we really need to know the cause(s) of the ageing of cells and body tissues. We need to know whether cells age simply because there is an inadequate **somatic effort**; that is, the energy that is put into bodily survival and growth is insufficient to maintain full cell function. If so, could we in some way increase our somatic effort? Or is there, as some scientists believe, a programmed death plan for each cell type?

Summary of Section 2.2

Biology tends to focus on physical characterizations and is concerned with the diminishing ability to maintain homeostasis in old age.

2.3 Biological theories of cellular ageing

The idea of programmed cell death emerged in the 1960s as a consequence of work undertaken by Hayflick. The suggestion was that each cell contained a biological 'time bomb', set to auto-destruct at a pre-arranged hour. Hayflick reached this conclusion after studying the ability of human fibroblasts ('fibre cells' – Book 1) to divide when grown outside the body in a culture medium. Cells are isolated and placed in culture dishes that contain the full range of nutrients necessary for growth. This is known as **tissue culture**. The cells he studied stopped dividing after about 50 divisions. If the cells were frozen for 20 years they would 'remember' how many divisions they still had left and use up their quota. There have been various criticisms of this work, not least of which is the observation that cells growing in culture dishes are a far cry from the natural situation. Indeed, most mammalian cells are very difficult to grow in culture (even keeping them alive can be a problem, which has consequences for organ donation). So it may be that the number of divisions has more to do with what can be achieved in culture than with what happens in the body. Recently, a variation of this theory has re-emerged suggesting that cells are genetically programmed to die unless they are continuously stimulated by chemical signals from other cells. Failure to provide these signals could occur at any time and this would lead to cellular ageing and ultimately death. Hayflick's original theory would suggest that, in the absence of accidental death, programmed death would occur at about the same time in all individuals of a species and hence there would be a typical lifespan with not much variation between individuals.

All other theories of ageing see the processes involved as being random and unplanned. In essence, they all involve types of cellular damage occurring, often no more than small inefficiencies that have a slow but ultimately fatal, cumulative effect. We will examine these ideas in more detail in Section 2.6, but first we need to know a little of what characterizes aged cells.

Summary of Section 2.3

Biological theories of cellular ageing are of two types: (1) programmed cell death suggests each cell has a finite pre-determined lifespan; (2) random damage theories suggest cells age as a consequence of damage leading to accumulated metabolic inefficiencies and errors.

2.4 Cellular changes with age – what is meant by an aged cell?

All cells undergo some changes with age. In our own bodies there are some cells that are frequently renewed and others that are long-lived, so the concept of an aged human cell does not correlate with the chronological age of the cell. In a matter of days a short-lived cell shows the same signs of ageing as will ultimately appear in a long-lived cell years later.

❑   Give an example of a cell that is short-lived and rapidly replaced by other similar cells.

▪   From Chapter 3 of Book 1, you may recall that epidermal cells of the skin are constantly being sloughed off and replaced. Other examples of cells that are constantly being replaced in the body are red blood cells (Book 3, Chapter 2) and the cells that line the gut (Book 3, Chapter 3) (See Figure 2.5).

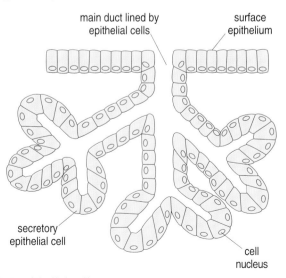

Figure 2.5   Gut epithelial cells.

❏   Give an example of a type of cell that cannot be replaced after birth and hence is long-lived.

▧   The neurons of the central nervous system (Figure 2.6).

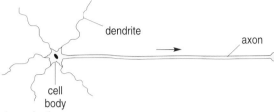

Figure 2.6   A typical neuron.

Irrespective of the chronological age of a cell or its nature, there are a number of changes that characterize older cells. In general these changes stem from a slowing down of cellular metabolism. You will recall that the constituents of a cell are constantly changing. For example, substances such as hormones, neurotransmitters and enzymes are produced in response to current requirements and, ideally, output matches demand. In the older cell this cannot always be achieved. Cellular components that are no longer required are broken down into smaller constituents for recycling but the rate of turnover of these essential components declines with age. It is the inefficient turnover of proteins that produces one 'marker' of ageing, namely granules of **lipofuscin** (ly-po-few-sin). Lipofuscin is a yellow pigment. It is a lipoprotein (it has both a lipid and a protein component) and it is the byproduct of inefficient recycling of protein. Figure 2.7 shows lipofuscin granules in a liver cell of a 62-year-old person.

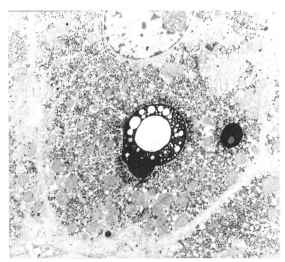

Figure 2.7   Electron micrograph of a liver cell ($\times$ 1 300). The dark lipofuscin granules are clearly visible and occupy a considerable proportion of the cell volume. (The pale structure at the top is the cell nucleus – the dark structure in the middle with the white centre is an artefact produced by the preparation procedure.)

Lipofuscin is found in all old cells. When added to cells in culture it slows their metabolic rate.

❏   If lipofuscin also has this effect on living cells in the body, what are the consequences for cell function?

■   As lipofuscin accumulates, the rate of manufacture and recycling of proteins will further decrease, and there will be a consequent slowing of cellular metabolism.

Older cells also show an increase in the number of lysosomes.

❑   What are the constituents of lysosomes and what is their role in the cell?

■   Lysosomes contain digestive enzymes. These are used to break down old organelles as well as the cell debris that accumulates in a microbial infection or during wound healing (Book 1, Chapter 3).

Because of their potentially destructive effects, it is not surprising that the accumulation of both lysosomes and lipofuscin in aged cells has been linked to cell death. But we cannot say whether their presence there is the cause or the effect of cell ageing. In fact, there is no actual evidence for a causal role, and their increased appearance could be related to some other, unknown, event. Indeed Figure 2.8 shows that whilst there is, overall, an increase in lipofuscin content in older heart cells, the relationship between age and lipofuscin content is rather weak.

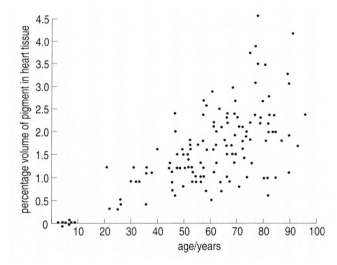

Figure 2.8   Scatter diagram showing the relationship between age in humans and the lipofuscin content of heart muscle cells. Notice that the relationship becomes quite weak (the points are more scattered) among the oldest old, some of whom have lipofuscin levels similar to those of 20–30-year-olds, whilst others have levels more than 10 times as great.

Another characteristic of older cells is the observation of an increased number of chromosomal abnormalities and of structurally altered proteins.

❑   How might these two observations be linked?

■   An abnormal chromosome is suggestive of loss or damage to DNA and because much of the DNA codes for protein the outcome might be an abnormal protein (Book 1, Chapter 3).

This undoubtedly does happen, although most of the damaged coding DNA would fail to yield *any* product. On the other hand, many proteins are long-lasting and can be altered *after* manufacture. In particular, the ubiquitous protein collagen (the most abundant protein in mammals) shows an altered structure with age: the cross-linking of collagen molecules increases as we get older.

This results from a spontaneous reaction between certain sugars (such as glucose and fructose) and part of an amino acid component of the polypeptide chain. This reaction is called glycation (and was discussed in Book 3, Chapter 7). Altering the structure of collagen can have a number of outcomes dependent upon the molecular site of the alteration. For example, the ability to break down and recycle collagen will be impaired if there is a structural alteration at any site where enzymes need to attach to initiate these processes. The tissue in which collagen is located is also relevant.

Cross-linked collagen has decreased elasticity and in most organs, such as kidney and skin, there is a potential for functional deterioration.

❑   How would the kidney and skin be functionally affected if their collagen content was more rigid?

■   The filtration properties of the kidney would be adversely affected (Book 3, Chapter 5). Skin loses its elasticity and this may affect wound healing (Book 1, Chapter 3).

Glycation can affect any protein and problems occur if the affected site is a receptor site where other molecules attach. So glycation could be responsible for many of the instances of decreased tissue sensitivity to hormones with age.

❑   Can you give an example of such decreased tissue sensitivity?

■   There is a decline in the sensitivity of the ovarian follicles to stimulation by pituitary hormones in women of around 40 years and older (Book 4, Chapter 2).

This description of age-related cellular changes does not seem to present too frightening a catalogue of defects and you may feel quite cheered and hopeful that medical science will soon offer us some methods of preventing even these changes from occurring. One drawback is that, whilst we can describe them, we really do not have a clear idea of what mechanisms actually initiate these changes. We will return to a consideration of some possible mechanisms in Section 2.6.

In the meantime, we have to accept that as we age we are unable to maintain a full range of bodily functions; we are often operating close to the limits of our reserves and are less able to respond effectively to challenges from the environment. Ultimately this limits our ability to survive. Let us describe the actual bodily changes that occur and see whether they can be prevented or whether their effects can be ameliorated.

From general knowledge you should be able to make a list of changes that occur as people age.

Do this now and for each age-related change say whether you think this change is inevitable. In other words, will every old person suffer this change?

Summary of Section 2.4

Aged cells are characterized by: (i) the presence of lipofuscin, a yellow pigment which is the by-product of inefficient protein metabolism; (ii) increased numbers of lysosomes; (iii) increased numbers of chromosomal abnormalities; (iv) increased occurrence of structurally altered proteins and (v) decreased sensitivity to hormones.

2.5 Age-associated changes

2.5.1 The skin

Wrinkles are almost synonymous with ageing. This does seem to be a change that affects every one of us as we get older.

❑   Can you remember how wrinkles are formed (Book 1, Chapter 3)?

◼   In the dermis there are bundles of collagen fibres. Collagen is a fibre that has tremendous strength and elasticity, but the elasticity decreases gradually as we age.

Figure 2.9 An 86-year-old woman.

In addition, the proportion of collagen in the skin increases and the water content of the connective tissue decreases. This, coupled with the thinning of the fat layer just below the surface of the skin leads to the rather 'loose' and dry texture of ageing skin (Figure 2.9). As far as we know at present these changes are not reversible although many a fortune must have been made in persuading people that the application of creams containing collagen and 'moisturisers' would rejuvenate their tissues.

The age-associated changes in the skin do not pose much threat to our health and well-being, but you will remember that dry and itchy skin was one of the few complaints that troubled Miss Hamish.

❑   What might cause her dry and itchy skin, and how might these symptoms be relieved?

■   This might be a result of oestrogen deficiency in which case HRT could be beneficial (Book 4, Chapter 2). In her case, though, we know that the dermatologist had been unable to find a cause of the itchiness.

The appearance of an ageing skin has become associated with unattractiveness, especially by some women, and can therefore have harmful affects on their sense of well-being. In contrast, a 'glowing' tan is highly prized in some modern cultures. Ironically, prolonged sunbathing by light-skinned people increases the damage caused by ultraviolet radiation from the sun, the long-term effects of which are premature skin ageing, as well as increased susceptibility to skin cancer.

2.5.2 Muscles, cartilage and bones

The gait of older people is often distinctive. They do not bound or skip along, the way that a child does, nor do they stride out like someone in the prime of life. Creaking joints, stiff muscles and aching bones are often held to blame. Whilst such observations are common, are they universal? The prima ballerina Margot Fonteyn was still executing physical feats at 60 which many people half her age would find impossible to accomplish. To what extent is this a case of 'use it or lose it'? Swimming was very important to Miss Hamish and was something she missed a great deal when her cataracts kept her at home.

There is evidence that muscle fibres are lost as we age. Up to 30% may disappear between the ages of 30 and 80. The explanation for this loss may be found in a parallel loss of the motor neurons innervating the muscle fibres. Studies suggest that both types of cell die if not used.

❑   Are either of these types of cell replaced by normal cell division in the mature person?

■   No, these cells cannot be replaced.

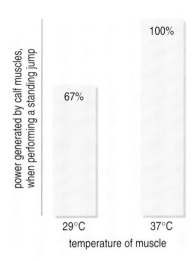

Figure 2.10 Power output of human calf muscles at different temperatures.

With the loss of muscle fibres comes a diminution of strength. This means that older people may be unable to perform quite ordinary tasks such as opening heavy swing-doors, carrying heavy packages, opening screw top bottles and jars. This affects well-being and confidence, but the good news is that these changes are not inevitable or irreversible; muscle *performance* can be improved through exercise at any age and this can compensate for loss that has already been sustained.

❑   Can you suggest what difficulties might prevent an older person from taking sufficient exercise?

◼   There are many factors which inhibit older people's access to enjoyable exercise, e.g. lack of transport, not being able to afford to pay and embarrassment.

❑   Look at Figure 2.10 and suggest what else should be done to ensure the full use of available muscle power.

◼   Keep warm!

This may partially explain the popularity, amongst the well-off, retired citizens of the British Isles, of spending the winter in warmer climes. But there are many older people for whom keeping warm presents real problems.

Loss of muscle fibres is not inevitable, but bone mass reduces with age in both men and women. This is a result of mineral loss and a reduction of the organic matrix of bone.

❑   Which element is of greatest importance in providing the strength that we associate with bone?

◼   Calcium (Book 2, Chapter 2).

The loss of calcium results in a reduction of bone density. In compact bone the rate of bone loss exceeds the rate of deposition of new material, so that the outer shell of bone becomes thinner. Trabecular bone loses the horizontal spars of the reinforcing network, thus weakening the bone. A major factor in the determination of bone mass in old age is the amount of bone at maturity. Also, the rate of bone loss varies from person to person.

Once again there is tremendous individual variability and some older people have more bone than younger people. The underlying factor responsible for the loss of calcium from bones seems to be age-related changes in calcium metabolism. Older people absorb less of the calcium that they consume in their diet, owing to age-associated changes in the absorptive cells lining the gut. In addition, they often suffer from vitamin D deficiency.

❏   Why might an older person suffer from vitamin D deficiency?

■   There are two possible sources of vitamin D. It can be absorbed from food, so changes in the cells lining the gut will result in less efficient uptake of vitamins from the diet. Alternatively, it can be manufactured in the skin using sunlight to activate this synthesis. However, many older people spend less time in the open air; as a result of this, and because of changes in the skin, they could fail to obtain adequate amounts of vitamin D from this source.

❏   In what way is this relevant to a discussion of bone loss?

■   Vitamin D facilitates the transport of calcium through the lining of the small intestine into the blood, and it controls the deposition of calcium in bones. So a reduction in available vitamin D results in the slowing down of new bone growth to replace old bone as it is destroyed.

Reduction in bone mass creates more of a problem for women. In general, men have greater bone mass at maturity than women and the difference in bone mass between the sexes with age is partly accounted for by this. On average, women start out with less bone and so they reach the point where bone loss is critical relatively more rapidly than men. It is also the case that changes in calcium metabolism are more pronounced in post-menopausal women than they are in men of the same age. Women in older age groups excrete more calcium in their urine than they take in from their diet. This appears to be a result of calcium being withdrawn from bones because of disturbances in the various hormones involved in the normal formation of bone.

Age-associated changes in bones can pose a serious threat to health, especially in women. The condition of **osteoporosis** is said to exist when the level of bone mass falls below a critical point and this results in an increased risk of fractures. In some research studies, treatment with oestrogen has had a beneficial effect on calcium balance, and has reduced the rate at which bone density was lost in older women. However, the results are contradicted by other studies and so the use of HRT remains controversial. Half an hour's brisk exercise daily is reported to reduce bone loss in post-menopausal women and ensuring adequate dietary calcium is also a sensible measure. Once again there is disagreement over what 'adequate' might be! But as a guide, a pint of skimmed milk contains about 700 mg which should meet the daily needs of most older people.

For many older people like Lily Bradshaw, it is not their bones and muscles that cause them problems but their joints. Joints that are stiff in the mornings and ache when the weather is damp, stiff and swollen fingers, and back pain, are all symptoms reported by many of those in the over-60 age group (and quite a few who are younger!). Not every old person experiences these problems but they are common, and we know that joints are susceptible to particular kinds of damage as they age, simply because of the job that they do. Cartilage undergoes constant wear and repair and tendons are subjected to regular mechanical stresses.

The ability to maintain tissues in the joint alters with age, but it is often difficult to identify intrinsic age-related biological changes, and distinguish them from the results of repairs following minor injuries or reactions to persistent mechanical stresses, such as poor posture or repetitive actions. The thinning of joint cartilage that occurs with age may be due in part to wear and tear, rather than to any underlying age-related changes in the cells that produce new cartilage. However, one exceedingly common age-related trait is the appearance of bone cells in cartilage. This is not necessarily associated with any observable disability, but it can make joints less mobile. The deposition of bone in the costal cartilage (this is the cartilage joining the ribs and breastbone) makes these joints more rigid.

❑   What function will this affect?

◼   Breathing. If there is less mobility between the ribs and the breastbone, rib movements will be restricted during breathing. This will be most noticeable when greater physical exertion is attempted or when the respiratory system is stressed, for example when suffering from a cold, bronchitis or similar respiratory tract infection.

Loss of water from the fibrous cartilage of the shock–absorbing discs between the vertebrae of the backbone is another problem, which can lead to a reduced ability to bear or lift weight. (It is also responsible for the 'shrinking' of older people.)

The catalogue of possible changes in the structural fabric of the body does not in itself represent inevitable disabilities, but it does make the individual more susceptible to diseases of the muscles, joints and skeleton and less able to recover from accidents and injury. A report by the Office of Population Censuses and Surveys (OPCS, 1988) showed that disorders of the muscles and bones were responsible for about 40% of all physical disability in British adults. Conversations about back problems can be almost as frequent as discussions about the weather when you are with friends who are over 40.

❑   Apart from discomfort, what might be a consequence of these problems for older workers?

◼   Time off work may be necessary, maybe leading to the loss of a job.

The 1993 OPCS report states that 5.5 million working days were lost from these causes. This can represent considerable loss of income to families, e.g. of the self-employed. There are also increased costs to the NHS and industry.

Loss or reduction of mobility and failing strength bring very real distress. The frustration of not being able to participate in sporting events or even to keep pace with others when out rambling can lead to a downward spiral where the condition is exacerbated by a failure to take any exercise at all. At the same time, social contact is reduced, with further negative effects in terms of well-being. In a similar way, hobbies may be harder to pursue, particularly those that require manual dexterity, e.g. embroidery, woodwork, drawing and painting – even card games may present difficulties. Just when there is more time for hobbies they may become less accessible.

2.5.3 The nervous system

Many older people complain of memory loss but this is certainly not true of all. Indeed the store of memories and associated wisdom can be regarded as one of the benefits that old age brings. And have you noticed the age structure of most governments?

Neurons are not able to replicate so they cannot be replaced if they die. The brain loses weight as it ages, weight loss beginning at around 50 years but, as always, there is considerable variation between individuals. To give you some idea of the extent of the loss, the average weight of the normal young adult male brain is about 1 400 g, but by 65 this may have dropped to 1 200 g. Comparable figures for women are about 100 g less. This is because women, on average, weigh less than men; brain weight is proportional to body weight. So a large woman has a bigger brain than a small man. Loss of brain weight can be accounted for by loss of water. As you might expect, this is loss of intracellular water. As a consequence of this shrinkage, the brain ventricles (Book 2, Chapter 3) occupy more space.

Reports of huge cell losses in the brain were made in the 1950s and have passed into popular lore. Later research has shown that the claims that millions of neurons die daily from birth onwards is just not true. There is a progressive loss of neurons with age, but it is far more modest than was originally believed. The numbers of cells in the brain are measured in billions, so the fact that it is estimated that cell loss from the cerebral cortex runs into something like 100 000 neurons every day of adult life is but a drop in the ocean. In addition to the usual individual variation, there is variation in the areas that sustain the greatest cell loss. The region of the brain that suffers greatest cell mortality is the cerebellum.

❑   What kinds of functional loss would this lead to?

◼   The cerebellum is involved in the coordination of movement (Book 2, Chapter 3). If the cell loss results in a functional deficit it could exacerbate any difficulties being experienced as a consequence of impaired muscle, bone or joint function.

The cerebellum loses up to 2% of its neurons per decade for the first six decades. Thereafter a healthy brain shows further loss, still without ill effects. Where an individual has an abnormal loss of cerebellar cells, they exhibit a condition known as ataxia (Book 2, Chapter 4).

❏   Describe the behaviour of someone with ataxia.

▧   Their most pressing practical problem is an inability to stop movements at the appropriate and desired position. So they walk awkwardly (often giving the impression of being drunk) and have trouble reaching for, and grasping objects.

Another region particularly prone to neuron loss is the substantia nigra.

❏   What is the consequence of a high cell loss from this region?

▧   A condition called Parkinson's disease develops. Here, movement is difficult to initiate. It is slow and muscles have both a rigidity and tremors (Book 2, Chapter 4). Remember the problems and embarrassment this caused Lily?

A person with either ataxia or Parkinson's disease has lost the ability to fine tune movement.

Despite cell loss, in healthy brains there are active repair processes which enable cells around a dead cell to make compensatory contacts. Axons branch and dendritic connections become more bushy. Thus it is possible that the functions of the lost cells are retained. It is important to remember that the vast majority of over-60s do not suffer from neurological disease. Lily, aged 74, and Miss Hamish, at nearly 90, were as mentally alert as many people half their age.

Psychological testing shows that older people often have more difficulty with hand to eye coordination, absentmindedness and other memory deficits. On the plus side, higher-level cognitive processes such as thinking and reasoning are judged to improve with age (though not indefinitely)! The extent to which these changes are observed in individuals is varied and the consequent effect upon health and well-being is equally as variable.

2.5.4 Sight

As we get older it becomes much more difficult to read small print, especially in dim light. In fact it becomes difficult to read any print without holding the printed page further and further away from the eye, until we eventually run out of arm and have to resort to reading glasses!

❏   Would this characteristic have altered the biological fitness of our ancestors?

▧   No, it is very unlikely that an inability to see fine detail close to the face would affect their ability to survive, or to procreate! You might also assert that only our more recent ancestors lived for long enough to be afflicted by the loss of near sight.

The lens loses its ability to change focus because it grows throughout life, adding fibres of proteins called crystallins. By the time we are 50-60 years old, it is almost impossible to change the shape of the lens because of its size and structure, and whilst many distant objects may be in sharp focus, near objects are blurred. There may also be changes in the structure of some crystallins, which can result in the formation of an opaque covering of the lens. This is known as a cataract. Although it can cause blindness, treatment is effective and restores sight. You will remember how Miss Hamish's health and well-being were adversely affected before her cataracts were operated on.

The pigments found in the rods and cones (the light-sensitive cells in the eye) absorb light and thereby register a 'picture' of the world around us. These so-called photo pigments consist of retinol, which is a complex lipid of very similar composition to vitamin A, covalently linked to a protein of a type known as an opsin. Lipofuscin can be detected in the rods and cones of children as young as 10 years; by the age of 24, lipofuscin occupies about 8% of the volume of these cells and by 80 it is over 20%.

❏   What are the possible functional consequences of this accumulation of lipofuscin?

▓   As lipofuscin accumulates, the rate of manufacture and recycling of the visual pigments decreases. Any defective or damaged pigment will remain in place longer, making the rods and cones more susceptible to the effects of cumulative damage. This contributes to the deterioration of vision in old age.

Slowing of other metabolic processes in the eye also occurs, including those that prevent or repair damage from radiation. It is a functional hazard that our eyes are exposed to the physical effects of sunlight. Any lessening of the effectiveness of mechanisms that prevent damage from this source of radiation causes cumulative damage that mistakenly may be attributed to the ageing process.

Although not all old people have any visual impairment, the changes in the proteins of the eye do mean that reading in low light intensity is difficult and glare from the page needs to be avoided when using a stronger light source. The use of sunglasses or a shady hat helps to avoid glare when out of doors. Not only is this more comfortable, but the wearing of sunglasses is protective too, lessening the damage from ultraviolet radiation. These changes to the eyes are normal and should not cause any distress. On the other hand, most older people notice that their night vision is less good, or at least that it takes longer to adapt to the dark and this has consequences for night driving. The headlights of oncoming cars overstimulate the visual pigments and it takes a long time for them to recover, effectively blinding the driver. This means that older car drivers start to avoid night driving and this can severely curtail their social lives, especially in winter.

2.5.5 Hearing

Hearing loss is a common, but not a universal, feature of old age. When it does occur, it can be associated with degeneration of sensory cells in the inner ear and/or the neurons of the auditory nerve. Some types of hearing loss have a familial tendency and hence probably have a genetic basis.

❑   Is there an alternative explanation?

■   There could be an environmental effect on hearing that is common to family members, such as living close to a major road or working in the same (noisy) industry such as coal mining or an iron foundry.

It is easy to show that hearing is damaged by persistent exposure to loud noises such as artillery fire or loud disco music, but less obvious that everyday noises, from traffic or even the continuous hum from a computer for example, slowly destroy sensory cells. Comparative studies of people who live in non-industrial societies suggest that high-tone hearing loss (a universal feature of Western societies) is due to ambient noise levels. It is difficult to know whether the hearing loss commonly measured in elderly people is the outcome of age-associated changes or simply the result of having lived a long time in our noisy Western environment.

Hearing loss is probably the most isolating of the possible deficits of old age.

Do you know an older person whose hearing has deteriorated? What impact do you think it has had on their health and well-being?

2.5.6 Taste and smell

Whilst many older people report a fading of their sense of taste and smell, there does not seem to be much evidence of efforts to investigate this in any systematic way. It is known that taste buds (groups of taste-sensitive cells and supporting cells on the tongue) which number about 10 000 in adults, degenerate from the age of 45 onwards. It is also known that the reduced ability to detect odours accentuates the lessening of ability to discern subtle differences in flavours. This reflects on the pleasures of life in a number of ways.

❑   What difference would it make to your life if you had a very diminished (or total loss of your) sense of taste and smell?

■   Whatever your answer is, it is of course right. Our perceptions of these sensations are intensely individual and the value we place on them is very personal. However, some common themes emerge in that taste has a considerable influence on our judgement of the worth of food items and smell tends to affect our inter-personal relationships.

❑   Make a list of the dangers for an older person that you think might
     attend a loss of taste and smell.

■   Being unable to smell might mean that the smell of gas would not be
     detected. Older people are prone to not renewing old domestic
     appliances because it 'doesn't seem worth it', and so they put
     themselves at risk from faulty equipment. Absentmindedness could
     also result in a gas appliance being turned on and then not ignited.
     Similarly, cooking food can be left unattended and the smell of
     burning pass undetected. Food may be eaten despite being in poor
     condition because the 'off' flavours are not noticed.

The loss of enjoyment of food can lead, particularly for someone who lives
alone, to a failure to bother to prepare proper meals and hence to an
impoverished or inadequate diet. It can also seem that fate is dealing a cruel
blow when the small pleasures of life, the taste of food and the smell of
flowers (Figure 2.11) cannot be enjoyed to the full.

Figure 2.11 Scented *Clematis* climbing a house wall.

It may seem strange, but the fact that older people are not good at
recognizing their own thirst has been attributed to changes in taste
sensitivity. The consequence of this is that in many cases older people do not
drink enough. To some extent we learn how much to drink (Book 3, Chapter
6) but as we age our kidneys function less well and excrete a more dilute
urine. So we need to drink relatively more to avoid dehydration.

2.5.7 Temperature regulation

Temperature regulation is of fundamental importance in the maintenance of
bodily function. One of the places where temperature perception occurs is in
the skin. Cold receptors are highly dependent on a good oxygen supply to
function correctly. An age-associated deterioration in the blood supply to the
skin may lead to a decline in function of the temperature receptors. This,
coupled with alterations in the nerves controlling vasoconstriction and
vasodilation, will also alter the way that the body regulates temperature.

❏   Are there other aspects of the biology of ageing that could alter an older person's ability to regulate temperature satisfactorily?

■   The decreased sensitivity of tissues to hormones could have an effect, as has been described for menopausal women (Book 4, Chapter 2). Muscular activity generates heat, but many old people, like Lily, have reduced mobility for a variety of reasons. In her case, pain from varicose veins and arthritis was very debilitating.

In very cold weather the inability to regulate body temperature can lead to hypothermia which has resulted in a number of deaths in older people.

❏   What are the other non-biological factors which are responsible for an older person becoming hypothermic?

■   Living in a cold damp house or flat with little or no heating, or not being able to afford fuel, are considered more likely to be responsible for deaths due to hypothermia than the age-associated changes in the ability to regulate body temperature. Having someone else to light a fire or fill a hot water bottle if your mobility is restricted can make a world of difference. In other words, your social circumstances play a vital role in keeping warm.

Once again we are aware that the individual's experience of age and the healthiness of their later years is dependent on far more than their biology. Nevertheless, in the next section we are going to delve into the cellular events associated with ageing and survey some of the mechanisms that have been proposed as the agents of change.

Summary of Section 2.5

1   As we age we are aware of a number of changes to our bodies. The most obvious of these changes are:

(a) the skin becomes wrinkled and dry;

(b) mobility becomes more difficult.

2   This reduction in mobility can be attributed to any combination, or all, of the following:

(a) weaker musculature resulting from muscle fibre loss;

(b) bones becoming more brittle as they lose both minerals and organic matter. If the bone mass falls below a critical level, the individual is said to be suffering from osteoporosis;

(c) joints becoming stiff and achey, often a result of damage to cartilage.

3   Older people may have impaired cognitive and motor skills. But the most striking examples of this are actually disease conditions such as Parkinson's and ataxia, which are more common in the elderly than in young people.

4   Deterioration of vision is an almost universal experience amongst the elderly.

5   Impaired hearing is very common in old age.

6   The sense of taste and smell are reported to diminish and the former may account for some older people drinking too little.

7   Older people may not keep themselves warm enough, for socio-economic reasons. Ultimately this can result in death from hypothermia when an already frail body is unable to maintain the core body temperature by normal homeostatic mechanisms.

2.6 Biological explanations for the mechanisms of cellular ageing

The fact that individuals vary so greatly in the way that they age immediately suggests that more than one mechanism may be operating. The mechanisms that are about to be described are not, for the most part, mutually exclusive. As you might expect, explanations cannot be confined to the merely biological, but instead range from the action of genes to the effects of lifestyle and environment. Of course, much of the scientific research has been carried out on species with short lifespans – rats and fruit-flies – rather than on humans.

2.6.1 Genes

The overwhelming evidence from animal studies, where different strains have been selectively bred for long or short lifespans, is that the interaction of many genes is responsible for this characteristic. That this is also true for humans seems likely from studies of a rare disorder called *progeria*. In this condition the body ages physically very rapidly over the first few years of life, the child rarely living beyond 5 years. The study of progeroid human cells indicates that several thousand genes can influence the onset and development of the senile appearance (Martin, 1978). This does not rule out the possibility that, in some individuals, it could be the activity of just one gene that is responsible for major age-related changes. In the roundworm a single recessive gene has been found, possession of which can double the worm's lifespan (Friedman and Johnson, 1988).

Throughout our lives there is a considerable turnover of many of our **somatic cells** (soma means body, so somatic cells are all the body cells excepting the reproductive cells). Sometimes, in the process of chromosomal replication (mitosis), mistakes are made and imperfect copies of DNA result. These are normally repaired immediately but, as already mentioned (Section 2.4), the efficiency of metabolic processes decreases with age. A somatic mutation occurs when the DNA error is not corrected and this altered DNA will be passed to descendant cells of this lineage. It is believed that somatic mutations are a *consequence* of ageing and are not responsible for its onset. They are, however, important causes of age-associated diseases, particularly cancers.

2.6.2 Free radicals

The idea that effects of free radicals on cellular processes are a core mechanism responsible for cellular ageing has gained wide acceptance. Free radicals are groups of highly reactive atoms, the byproducts of normal cellular metabolism. Although normally short-lived, they can change the structure of other molecules in the cell by oxidation. This only happens when the free radicals are not deactivated by special enzymes such as catalase and superoxide dismutase (Figure 2.12), but when it does happen they are like a loose cannon ball; their effects can be devastating because they are random and unpredictable. Damage to long-lasting proteins, such as the crystallins of the eye, could be due to free radicals directly altering the protein, rather than a consequence of somatic mutations.

There are a number of pieces of evidence supporting the centrality of free-radical damage in ageing.

1   Post-mortem results show that older human brains contain relatively more oxidized protein than is found in younger specimens (Young, 1993).

2   Experiments performed by John M. Carney of the University of Kentucky Medical Centre in 1991, established that a chemical that deactivates free radicals improves the performance of old gerbils in memory tests, and also lowers the levels of oxidized proteins in their brains.

3   One long-lived strain of fruit-fly produces a particularly active variant of superoxide dismutase.

4   Rodents that had exercised to exhaustion had at least trebled levels of free radicals, as well as damaged mitochondria, in their cells.

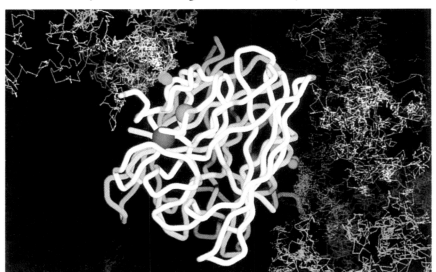

Figure 2.12   Model of a molecule of the enzyme superoxide dismutase (blue and white structure at the centre). The copper (green) and zinc (mauve) atoms which form part of this enzyme help in the break-up of the free-radical substrate (small blue spheres).

❑   What relevance do mitochondria have for this theory?

▓   They are the site of the release of energy from glucose by oxidation which is a source of free-radical formation (Book 3, Chapter 7).

Prolonged exercise requires an increase in the amount of energy generated in the mitochondria by oxidation; this in turn generates more free radicals (the agents of oxidation), which damage cell function. Excessive exercise could seriously damage your health!

In a sense, the free radical theory of ageing implies that by virtue of our dependence on a fundamental chemical reaction (oxidation) against which we do not have a perfect defence, we start to age from the moment of conception. There will subsequently be wide variation in the ensuing damage, dependent on the types of molecules attacked and the particular cells that are affected. To a certain extent this may reflect our lifestyle; for example the athlete may suffer differently from the couch potato.

2.6.3 Lifestyle

There is evidence that lifestyle can have a very considerable effect on longevity but very little direct evidence that it has effects on cell ageing.

❑   Suggest some ways that lifestyle affects health and longevity.

▓   There have been many examples of factors that affect health and longevity given in this course, beginning with the mother's health and lifestyle during pregnancy (Book 1, Chapter 6). In our middle years the likelihood of accidental death is highest, for, although regular exercise is beneficial, some hobbies are more dangerous than others, such as deep-sea diving and horse riding. Use of certain substances shorten the lifespan, dramatically in the case of, say, heroin, or insidiously in smoking tobacco. Some issues linking diet and health were raised in Book 3, Chapter 7. In this present chapter we have indicated some of the socio-economic factors that may be responsible for Miss Hamish's longevity.

People who are interested in increasing the human lifespan have turned their attention to diet, since studies showed that rats on a restricted-calorie diet lived longer than those allowed unlimited access to food. Currently work is underway to investigate the effects of a low-calorie diet on non-human primates, but as yet there is no evidence that anyone who is presently between the extremes of obesity and starvation would lengthen their life by eating less (discussed in Audio sequence 2).

People who indulge in strenuous or dangerous sports run the risk of physical damage. Often the healing process is incomplete and they may suffer a less comfortable old age, being particularly prone to arthritis developing in previously damaged joints. This would not, in itself, shorten their lifespan. In fact many structures, including cartilage and teeth, experience increased wear and tear as individuals age. However, for most of us they last for as long as we need them. We do not die because our cells have worn out in normal day to day living. Those cells that do die and are not replaced, such as neurons, are initially present in abundance. In the next chapter we will discover that the reserve capacity of most organs is huge.

We are all very aware these days that there are toxins in the environment. Many of them are products of industrialization but others are found in the natural environment. The ability to make plant toxins safe in food preparation and the avoidance of toxic plants is part of our cultural inheritance. As we get older, the cells of our bodies accumulate toxins that are not excreted.

❑   Which organ has the primary role in detoxification?

▓   The liver (Book 3, Chapter 3).

The liver stores toxins that cannot be excreted. Despite the fact that the average liver volume falls by over a third during the lifespan, and that old liver cells have increased levels of lipofuscin and other inactive proteins, there is no evidence that liver function is impaired in old age unless there is damage due to excessive long-term alcohol consumption. It seems unlikely that cell ageing is a result of the accumulation of toxins.

The only thing that does seem reasonably certain is that ageing is a multi-factorial process, the result of an accumulation of minor inefficiencies and damage occurring at different times and in different parts of the body. Probably no two people age in the same way or for exactly the same reasons. Researchers remain hopeful that new insights will enable us to slow the rate of ageing and hence increase the normal life expectancy and well-being of the population. Some speculate that evolutionary theory might give us a better understanding of these processes.

Summary of Section 2.6

We do not know why cells start to age but suspect that there may not be a single mechanism. Research has shown that genes, free radicals and our individual lifestyles can each have a hand in the ageing processes.

2.7 Evolutionary theory and ageing

When we make comparisons with other species we see that humans are unique with regard to the proportion of individuals within the population who survive long enough to show clear signs of ageing. This is particularly true of affluent societies, as was discussed at the beginning of this chapter. It was pointed out earlier that we vary enormously from one to another in the particular signs of ageing that we display and in their order and onset. Some of these changes are unpleasant and debilitating, so it seems reasonable to wonder why natural selection has not resulted in a greater proportion of the population being free from those age-related characteristics that disadvantage them.

❑   Give some examples of age-related changes that are disadvantageous, and explain how they would disadvantage you.

■   Your list will reflect your current lifestyle in many ways and the items on your list will probably depend on your age. If you enjoy energetic sports such as squash or football, you might have cited loss of mobility preventing you from enjoying these sports and the associated social life. If your mobility is already somewhat reduced, you might be more concerned that reduced vision would prevent you from driving a car, or making use of public transport, and might hence result in a more isolated life. If we speculated about our distant ancestors we could imagine that both reduced vision and reduced mobility would affect their ability to hunt for or gather food.

Any individual who was less well equipped to compete for the resources essential for life would be at a disadvantage. The theory of natural selection predicts that those individuals, being less well adapted, would leave fewer surviving offspring. Over time, the proportion of the species that shares the adaptive characteristics rises (Book 1, Chapter 1).

❑   How then can these non-adaptive features persist? (Hint: Remember from Book 1, Section 1.8.2 that natural selection favours those characteristics that are both adaptive *and* are inherited by the organism's offspring.)

■   The characteristic features of ageing are 'beyond the reach' of natural selection because they have appeared after reproduction has started and will have already been passed on to the offspring, before they start to represent a disadvantage to the adult with the feature.

There are many different manifestations of ageing and if someone exhibits a characteristic that shortens their life and results in their leaving fewer children than other people, then their *biological fitness* has been reduced. So natural selection *would* be operating in this example. But, in general, we don't die from age-related causes whilst we are still capable of producing fertile gametes, bearing children and caring for them.

This brings us to a second feature that makes us unique. Human females lose the ability to ovulate and to bear children naturally at menopause, usually long before they die (Book 4, Chapter 2). Various arguments have been advanced to explain the evolution of menopause. Fundamental to these is the idea of the reproductive effort involved. For women, giving birth and feeding babies involves considerable physiological stress and the former can result in death. By preventing further reproduction, menopause removes the associated risks.

❑   Why is this adaptive? In what way will it increase women's biological
         fitness?

◼   The concept of biological fitness requires you to maximize the
         number of children that you raise to the point where they themselves
         can reproduce. Children are dependent upon their parents and
         particularly their mothers for food, warmth and protection for a long
         time. Remember too that reliable forms of birth control have only
         become available relatively recently. A woman who dies in childbirth
         leaves all her existing dependants at risk. If mothers continued
         having children throughout their lives, they would eventually
         undertake a birth that was so stressful that they would die, or be so
         severely weakened that they could not continue to care for their
         existing offspring. Thus, menopause is adaptive because it favours
         the survival of existing children at the expense of potential future
         children.

Another argument in support of menopause as an adaptive characteristic is
that post-menopausal women have a valuable contribution to make to
ensure that close relatives (kin) have successful pregnancies and that their
babies are properly cared for. The evidence for this can be gleaned from
animal studies showing that the larger the extended family of care-givers,
the higher is the rate of survival of infants born into it. The extended
families include older brothers and sisters, cousins, aunts and uncles and
grandparents (Figure 2.13). However, post-menopausal women may be of
particular value in the upbringing of such children because the evidence
(again from animal studies) is that breeding success increases with age;
parents get better at rearing their young with each successive breeding
episode.

Figure 2.13 Grandparents enjoying a caring role.

These arguments are based on an extension of the theory of natural
selection called **kin selection**. According to this hypothesis, genes that

cause a woman's reproductive activity to be switched off at a certain stage will be favoured by natural selection if, as a result of her post-reproductive behaviour, her progeny and those of other close relatives are more likely to survive. Her kin will tend to carry the same genes by descent, so the loss of reproductive potential by post-menopausal women is offset by their contribution to preserving the genes they share with their kin. Thus the reproductive changes at menopause are believed to be adaptive, unlike other age-related changes, which are beyond the control of natural selection.

Summary of Section 2.7

There are no known advantages of ageing. It is not an adaptive process that has evolved by natural selection. Menopause may be adaptive in preventing women from undertaking pregnancies throughout their lives. Without the menopause, the last-born children would not have their mothers around for long enough to rear them to the point of independence. A further benefit of menopause is that it allows women a time when they can offer their care-giver skills to close relatives.

2.8 Normal ageing: the need to take a wider view

Embedded in biological theories of ageing are issues of normality, but what is 'normal' ageing? Scientific attempts to chart the course of 'normal ageing' specifically try to 'control' for what are called **cohort effects**; that is those aspects of a person's biography which are common to the particular cohort or group to which they belong. The implication is that living through the **Depression**, say, will have an unnatural or abnormal effect on the ageing process. The danger here is that we set up a notion of what is normal or healthy ageing, and therefore disease and life events are seen as abnormal and unhealthy. This is what Antonovsky (1984) called the **pathogenic paradigm**. In contrast he preferred to see disease and stresses as the norm and assumed that most people experience varying degrees of ill-health.

In a very real sense, individuals age to the extent that they acquire poor health, and they remain young to the extent that they maintain good health (Scrutton, 1992). It is the concept of normal ageing which is difficult to define. Therefore, predictions of bodily changes by chronological age are unhelpful. Even a cursory acquaintance with older people will show that diversity is the case. Two people who are 70 years old can appear very different in terms of their looks and degree of physical and mental well-being. Biological age-associated changes need to be considered along with other changes that occur as we age. Some of these are social, some psychological. What can we learn from disciplines other than biology?

2.9 Sociological insights into ageing

As with biological theories of ageing there is no real consensus in the sociology of ageing. However, broadly speaking, sociologists are concerned with the impact of the social structure on ageing.

One group of sociologists, known as functionalists, view society as a social system with interdependent parts having their own particular role and function in order that the whole can work smoothly. They offer a rather benign view of ageing. For example, there is a **disengagement theory** (Cumming and Henry, 1961) which suggests that older people voluntarily withdraw from society in preparation for death and in order that society can continue to function. On the other hand, there is an **activity theory** (Havighurst, 1963) presenting a view that is almost the exact opposite of this, namely that older people need to be kept active and integrated into society in order that it may still function. Both these theories are putting forward notions of successful ageing. In terms of health, disengagement sees old age as a time of serene preparation for death, with the older person adjusting to the losses of old age. In contrast, activity theorists argue that well-being in old age is achieved by older people refusing to accept the limitations imposed upon them.

In contrast to these views, some gerontologists argue that older people do not disengage voluntarily but are involuntarily disengaged in order to make room for subsequent generations. They would also argue that activity theory is equally unrealistic for older people because the economic and political structure of society prevents many older people from maintaining any major activity in later life and that they are thus made **structurally dependent**.

2.9.1 Structural dependency

Many older people by virtue of compulsory retirement attract the label of dependency. As well as this so-called **structural dependency**, older people are labelled dependent if they are incapable, temporarily or permanently, of performing a range of actions which are assumed to be within the competence of most people (Johnson, 1993). If they are unable to carry out the normal activities of daily living such as washing, dressing, walking and talking, then they are said to be heavily dependent. The ageist assumption that old age inevitably involves 'dependency' is challenged by Johnson. In a discussion of dependency and interdependency, he points out that old age is frequently depicted as a time of dependency and that this is set against the supposed independence of younger people. He believes that by virtue of being human we are all interdependent and such dichotomies are unhelpful:

> *In complex societies the extent of interdependence is greatly increased.*
> *We are totally dependent on many strangers (who produce food, power,*
> *clothing etc.) as well as on those with whom we live, work and have*
> *other personal relations. These forms of universal dependence are*

acknowledged, but not encompassed in the usage of the word. The logic
for this appears to be that we are all contributors as well as receivers and
thus equal partners in a social contract. (Johnson, 1993)

Some older people's ability to be interdependent contributors is severely
restricted by their socio-economic circumstances.

2.9.2 A political economy of old age

A **political economy** approach to old age sees the unequal distribution of
wealth affecting the health chances of people in old age. Poverty and social
class determine the health experience of older people. Certainly the
relationship of patterns of morbidity reflect social inequalities to a great
extent in old age. As the Black Report notes:

In old age the relationship between income and the capacity to protect
personal health is stronger perhaps than at any other time in the life cycle,
and in general it is likely that individuals who are well endowed through
generous or index-linked pension schemes will lead the healthiest, the most
comfortable and the longest lives after retirement. These material fortunes
or misfortunes of old age are closely linked with occupational class during
the working life. To have secure employment and an above average
income when one is at work is to be better able to provide for one's
retirement. It is in this way that continuity in the distribution of material
welfare is sustained, and inequalities in health perpetuated, from the
cradle to the grave. (Townsend and Davidson, 1986)

Poverty is inextricably linked to socio-economic variables such as gender,
social class, marital status, educational level and housing, the effects of which
were clearly to be seen in the statistical data on morbidity shown in Table
2.1. The ethnic origin of older people is a factor which is hard to determine
in relation to health. In the UK, numbers of older people from minority
ethnic groups are still too small to feature in large national sample surveys.
But smaller surveys suggest that any negative effects on their health in old
age is more likely to be related to social disadvantage and social
discrimination than to any inherent physiological characteristics (Blakemore
and Boneham, 1993).

As well as the effects of poverty and social class, sociologists are also
concerned with social relationships.

❑   What would you expect to be the effect on health of loneliness and
       social isolation?

▨   Loneliness and social isolation threaten the well-being of older people
       and account for a good deal of mental illness in old age, particularly
       depression.

Elaine Murphy, a consultant who specializes in psychological problems in old
age, claims that the lack of a confidante in old age is one of the main reasons
why older people become depressed. Depression can set in motion a cycle of
self-neglect which leads to poor physical health. Social support is therefore
an important factor in maintaining health and well-being in old age.

2.9.3 Social support

The value of social support as a resource for maintaining health and well-being has long been recognized. In England, Brown and Harris (1978) emphasized the protective element in social support. It has also been claimed that it may directly influence mortality (Berkman and Syme, 1979). There are two main theories to explain how social support affects health. One is that it directly and intrinsically enhances health and well-being. The other is that it acts as a buffer or cushions people against the effects of stressful experiences and so helps them to cope with stress.

The direct effect is apparent when people feel loved and liked and are able to return that love and affection. This bolsters their self-esteem and so has a direct effect on their sense of well-being. The buffering effect comes from the sense of security derived from knowing that someone will be there to provide support in the event of distressing circumstances. This acts by protecting people from the pathogenic effects of stress. People who feel supported are able to redefine any potential harm which threatens as well as having another resource to rely on.

What do we mean by the term 'social support' and who provides it? Social support simply means the support that people give and take within close social relationships. This usually includes family, friends and neighbours. It is informal, unlike the formal support that might be given by statutory workers such as social workers and care assistants. There are two aspects to social support. One is the emotional impact of love, affection and affirmation and the other is the practical help and advice that people get from their social relationships. This is important, not just in terms of the actual help, but for knowing that there is someone there to call on in an emergency.

The increased risk of chronic conditions which give rise to unpleasant symptoms, such as pain or disability, in older people and especially women as they age, coupled with the increased likelihood of encountering bereavement, accompanied frequently with a loss of income, all indicate that practical and emotional support in old age is vital. At the same time, the available pool of social support may, through death, marital break-up or geographical mobility, be dwindling. Nevertheless, the bulk of practical support given to older people is largely informal and comes from kin.

It used to be a frequent assertion that families in Britain neglected their elderly kin. This generated a great deal of research in the 1980s which showed that, on the contrary, families took on the bulk of the care of older people (Figure 2.14). Those older people who were without families or had outlived their children in some cases, were most at risk. Nevertheless, there persists a myth in which older people in non-Western cultures are more greatly valued and cared for.

Figure 2.14 An extended family gathering.

2.9.4 Cultural effects

There is a great deal of anthropological evidence which would support this myth, but there is also much counter-evidence. We have accounts of societies where older people are powerful and revered for their wisdom and knowledge and we have accounts of others where older people are neglected because they are a burden which threatens the survival of the group. Three factors seem to determine the fate of older people in any society. One is their access to special knowledge. In societies which depended on an oral tradition of knowledge, old people acquired a privileged status because of their memories. Another is their access to material resources, so that where older people have access to land or wealth then their status is maintained. The third factor is the degree of **filial piety**, or sense of duty to parents, which exists within a society. Where this duty to care for ageing parents is prescribed either by religion or culture to children, then there is the guarantee that they will not be abandoned. However, this may not be a desirable state, especially if the older children lack independent economic resources. Although they may treat their parents with outward respect, this does not guarantee private goodwill.

Economic security and loving relationships seem to be the best predictors of health in old age. But there is also another dimension which is focused on the psychological make-up of the person. In the next section, we conclude this review of the perspectives on ageing offered by different disciplines, by looking at the insights given to us by psychologists.

Summary of Section 2.9

1   Sociological insights into ageing try to get away from identifying a
     normal physical course to ageing and instead focus on the impact of
     the social structure on ageing.

2   The term 'structural dependency' is used to indicate how many older
     people are rendered dependent because they are withdrawn from an
     active socio–economic life.

3   The result of unequal distribution of wealth adversely affects health
     status in old age.

4   Social support is considered as a resource which can enhance health
     and well–being directly by providing love, affection and help, and
     indirectly by acting as a buffer between the individual and a stressful
     situation.

5   Cultural factors can also determine the level of social support available
     to older people.

2.10 Psychological insights on ageing

Psychology has diverse roots and different strands all of which reflect a
different perspective on ageing.

Cognitive psychology is concerned with the development of intelligence.
The picture of ageing that this presents in many ways mirrors the
biological, with a period of rapid growth of abilities in the early part of life
followed by a period of stability followed by a long period of decline.
However, the problems identified with this approach, i.e. that it can be
culture-blind and decontextualized, are relevant to the picture it paints of
later life. The impression it gives is of an apparently inevitable descent into
a period of life when all cognitive abilities are impaired.

We know that this is not true for everyone. Social gerontologists take a view
that counters the negative connotations of old age presented by cognitive
psychology. They have prefered to focus on the ability of older people to
acquire wisdom (Slater, 1994).

Developmental psychology has been a more fruitful area in the study of
ageing, although Freud himself saw old age mainly in terms of its
proximity to death and was much less interested in later life than some of
his followers. Jung gave much greater importance to the second half of life
saying:

> *A human being would certainly not grow to be 70 or 80 years old if this
> longevity had no meaning for the species to which it belongs. The
> afternoon of human life must have significance of its own and cannot
> be merely a pitiful appendage to life's morning.*

and he goes on to draw out the implications for older people:

We cannot live the afternoon of life according to the programme of life's morning – for what was great in the morning will be little at evening, and what in the morning was true will at evening have become a lie. Ageing people should know that their lives are not mounting and unfolding, but that an inexorable inner process forces the contraction of life. For a young person it is almost a sin – and certainly a danger – to be too much occupied with himself; but for the ageing person it is a duty and a necessity to give serious attention to himself. After having lavished its light upon the world, the sun withdraws its rays in order to illumine itself. (Jung, 1933)

Jung believed that we are thoroughly unprepared for the second half of life and that our education for the first half of life is wholly unsuited to our needs in the second half.

In a similar vein, Erik Erikson's (1982) stages of life analysis see a distinctly different role for the later part of life. He has been most influential on the study of ageing. He developed notions of a 'healthy personality', extending the developmental approach into later life. He identified eight stages of growth, from birth to maturity, each with a list of traits which indicated 'healthy' or 'pathological' personality patterns, and a list of tasks to be fulfilled in order to reach each stage of development. The task of the last stage is to achieve

…ego integrity when one's life has meaning and order resulting in an acceptance of one's one and only life cycle as something that had to be and that, by necessity, permitted of no substitutions.

Those who reach old age feeling unfulfilled and cheated when reviewing their lives are least likely to experience feelings of well-being in old age.

Psychologists are often concerned with how individuals cope with life events, especially stressful life events and have tried to identify certain personality resources for coping.

2.10.1 Personality resources for coping

There is a characteristic of some people's personality which is quite difficult to define that is thought to act as a buffer, protecting them from the harmful effects of stress. Individuals are thought to deal with stressful life events first by experiencing and appraising the event and then by taking action to cope with the event. Kobasa *et al.* (1981, 1982) argue that this process is affected by someone's disposition or temperament. People with different temperaments perceive life events in different ways. Some will make an optimistic appraisal of the situation, by perhaps taking a longer-term view or seeing the event in a context which does not seem so bad. Then there are those who immediately feel sorry for themselves, whereas others recognize that there are people worse off than themselves. Seeing the glass as half-empty or half-full is a typical example. Depending on their personality dispositions, people will, in the light of their appraisal of the event, make an appropriate response. Kobasa *et al.* explain:

What particular personality dispositions mitigate the otherwise debilitating effects of stressful life events? Specifically, they are those that have the cognitive appraisal effect of rendering the events as not so meaningless, overwhelming, and undesirable, after all, and the action effect of instigating coping activities that involve interacting with and thereby transorming the events into a less stressful form rather than avoiding them.

Persons with personality dispositions of this sort posess a valuable aid in avoiding illness-provoking biological states. (Kobasa et al.*, 1982).*

Kobasa *et al.* (1982) define the characteristic which acts as a stress-resisting resource as *hardiness*. They claim that this has three important elements: commitment, control and challenge. Commitment is a tendency to get involved in events or encounters rather than remaining detached from them. People who are committed are more likely to try to understand an event and take action, rather than avoiding the situation. This puts them more in control of the event so that they are more able to influence the event, rather than feeling helpless. A sense of control helps people to feel that they are capable of transforming a stressful event into something which is less harmful. As well as having commitment and control, hardy people are more likely to relish the challenge of stressful life events, seeing changes as 'interesting incentives to grow rather than threats to security' (Kobasa *et al.*, 1982, p. 170).

By the time people reach old age, their hardiness will have been tested many times. As Peter Coleman, who has studied adjustment in later life, says:

If old age has a special character in this regard it is the likelihood of unwanted changes occurring, sometimes also in close proximity and often unprepared for. (Coleman, 1993)

Yet older people do cope with enormous changes and adjust to potentially quite devastating life events, such as loss of role or loss of a life-long partner, which can include the loss of a home and often loss of income. We tend to focus on the minority who do not cope well with these losses, as they are the ones who seek help or who give their relatives and friends cause for concern. It is more illuminating to study those who retain their equilibrium in the face of adversity than studying those who do not.

The concept of *stamina* has been identified by Elizabeth Colerick to describe the qualities that distinguish older persons who demonstrate emotional resilience despite age-related losses and life change (Colerick, 1985). Aspects of stamina here include mental vigour, vitality and endurance, as she explains:

High levels of stamina entail resilience and staying power: the strength (physical or moral) to withstand disease, fatigue or hardship. Although physical strength often wanes in later life, internal stamina reflects well-tested convictions that obstacles are surmountable and that personal growth is an outcome of personal struggle. (Colerick, 1985)

This concept of stamina is linked to the concept of hardiness. Hardy people are more likely to develop stamina in later life and feel confident that they can cope with the losses and changes that occur rather than feeling helpless. But one of the most important findings of Colerick's work is that education has a great deal of effect on stamina, so emphasizing the role that earlier social experiences play in later life. She concludes:

> *The boundaries of old age as a biological life stage are expanded to include a social and psychological past. (Colerick, 1985).*

In later life, a person's health status is – perhaps more clearly than at any other point in the lifespan – determined by this complex interaction of biology and biography. The cumulative effects of a lifetime and the durability of the human body will affect health chances in later life. Whatever measure of health is used, whether it is mortality, morbidity, physical function or physical and psychological well-being, it will be dependent on these two criteria, both at the macro level seen in differences between populations and at the micro level of differences between individuals.

At the risk of over-simplifying these interactions, it might be helpful to see biological characteristics as primary influences and sociological and psychological characteristics as secondary influences.

Summary of Section 2.10

1   Psychology offers several different explanations of the relationships between health and ageing. Although cognitive psychology focuses on diminishing intelligence, others see the acquisition of wisdom as a compensatory factor.

2   Explanations as to why one person copes well with old age and another doesn't have pointed to personality characteristics variously identified as hardiness, stamina and the ability to make adjustments.

2.11 Improving the health of an ageing population

Improvements in the health chances of all older people will only be made if the secondary as well as the primary influences are taken into account. There is therefore scope for improving the health and well-being of older people, but this means attacking poverty, poor housing, loneliness and lack of social support. Society's attitude to older people, the resources it is willing to commit and the level of social support that we are all prepared to give, will all affect the quality of life for everyone in old age. So, there is a price to pay if we are to improve the quality of life for older people. Many are now questioning whether, with the projected levels of ageing population growth, even our present levels of quality of life are in fact sustainable.

What are the choices that face society as it ages. Should we try to push out the limits of longevity? Or should we accept that there is a limit to the human lifespan and concentrate on creating a situation where people live in good health until a very short time before they die?

For die we will. This is the only certainty that the future holds for us all. Despite the best efforts of science, no-one has evaded death. Interestingly, although many artists and philosophers have played around with the idea of cheating death, it is not a prospect that holds much general appeal. The balance of opinion seems to find sympathy with the thoughts expressed in Janacek's opera, The Makropoulos Case, where the heroine Elina Makropoulos realizes, after 337 years of life and despite retaining her looks and talents, that her life is empty, lonely and without pleasure or warmth. For humans with their sense of awareness and self-knowledge this may be reason enough to die, but it doesn't explain why death occurs in all species.

If we look for universal life events, that is, events that occur in everyone's life, death is the only certainty. Try to imagine life without the death of any living organism.

❏   Can you envisage any problems that are raised if nothing dies?

▨   You might wonder what we would eat!

We obtain all our nutrients from other living things, plants or animals. On the other hand, most plants live without causing the death of others, yet even they are not everlasting.

❏   Why not? Apart from being eaten, how do plants die?

▨   You might have chosen a number of *physical* causes such as being frozen, drought-stricken or blown away.

The physical environment is not particularly benign! Accidental death is more or less inevitable at some point. So even if we had, theoretically, the ability to live for ever, in practice, we would be wiped out sooner or later. The hostility of the natural environment means that, for each individual, death is ultimately inevitable. Our ability to push out the limits of longevity is uncertain. It may be that the basis of the rectangularization of mortality is not sound.

❏   What is the basis of Fries and Crapo's rectangularization of mortality?

▨   It is based on the supposition that there is a maximum limit to the human lifespan which most people in developed countries now approach. At present we do not know whether investing resources in an attempt to increase the limits of longevity are futile.

❏   What was the second part of Fries and Crapo's thesis?

▨   It was the compression of morbidity.

A challenge currently facing us is to make the compression of morbidity a reality.

Moody (1995), writing in a gerontological journal, presents a challenging and speculative view of social change for the 21st century by suggesting that there are four possible options for an ageing society. One of these is to try to achieve a compresion of morbidity, another he calls the prolongation of morbidity, which is more or less the situation in Western societies at present, a third is a prolongevity or life extension option and the fourth he calls 'recovery of the Life World'. These are described below.

1 The compression of morbidity option

Here we accept that the human lifespan is fixed, but our goal is to eliminate the signs and symptoms of ageing that appear before the maximum age has been reached. Moody likens this to the 'Wonderful One-Horse Shay' in a poem by Oliver Wendell Holmes. This was built in such a way that every part of it 'aged' at the same rate and so everything wore out at the same time. One moment everything functioned perfectly, the next it simply dropped dead.

In order for us to achieve the 'wonderful one-horse shay' scenario we need to concentrate resources into medical research which would both eliminate premature deaths and those diseases which do not necessarily kill but which debilitate and threaten the quality of life in old age. In other words more resources should go into preventing the conditions which give rise to unpleasant symptoms but which are not necessarily life-threatening, such as arthritis and varicose veins. Money would also be spent on health promotion aimed at preventing premature deaths.

2 The prolongation of morbidity

This is the state of affairs which exists today, with resources concentrated on extending life. The unintended consequence of improved technology has become the 'failure of success', adding years to life but not life to years. An example of this is the increase in dementia as people reach their 80s and 90s. Moody warns that we may see the period of morbidity grow longer and the demand for 'elective death' grow more widespread. Already voluntary euthanasia and the 'right to die' is widely accepted (although not legal) with about 70% of people polled in the UK being in favour of it. But there are fears that this could lead to a dangerous slippery slope where quality of life arguments are used in favour of involuntary euthanasia and where older people are made to feel under pressure to opt for euthanasia if they become a burden to others.

3 Prolongevity: life extension

In this option, scarce resources should not be wasted on incremental gains in life expectancy or even in improving the quality of life but should concentrate on delaying the ageing process itself, for example by investing in the *Human Genome Project*. This is an international scientific collaboration that aims to examine all the DNA that makes up the human genome. The relevance of this for 'life extension' would be if an understanding of a gene's role in ageing could be exploited to delay or prevent ageing. One method might be by *gene therapy*, the term used to describe the technique of splicing-in 'superior' genes. Alternatively, drugs might ameliorate the adverse effects of gene products. Thus 'life extension' sees medicine moving to diagnosis and treatment of disease at its molecular level and away from treating organ failures and overt symptoms. Genetic diagnostic tests and the possibility of repairing disorders by gene therapy in pregnancy could be considerably cheaper than current medical interventions.

4 Recovery of the Life World

This option represents the direct opposite of the life extension option and proposes that longevity should be limited in any one generation for reasons of solidarity and inter-generational justice. This would be achieved through collective action, not individual choice. This option is ecologically motivated and based on arguments about the sustainability of large numbers of older people at the expense of younger people. This option then would oppose the technological imperative of extending life in favour of 'appropriate technology' such as that developed for care of the terminally ill.

❑   Which option would you favour and which do you think is most likely to happen?

■   Moody (1995) himself clearly favours the last option claiming that it sees the meaning of old age as something sustained from generation to generation, a participation in shared living and dying whereby we transcend the limits of individual life. Your favoured option may be different. We are rather attracted to the 'wonderful one-horse shay'– remaining fit and well a bit beyond three score years and ten and then departing without much fuss. However, we do seem set on the prolongation of morbidity path which is going to be hard to divert.

Many of the issues raised by these four options such as euthanasia and hospice care are taken up in the next chapter which looks at the broad issues of death and dying.

Objectives for Chapter 2

After completing this chapter you should be able to:

2.1 Define and use, or recognize definitions and applications of, each of the terms printed in **bold** in the text.

2.2 Identify the biological and socio-economic determinants of health in old age. (*Questions 2.1 and 2.2*)

2.3 Describe the biological changes that occur with age. (*Questions 2.2, 2.3 and 2.5*)

2.4   Discuss biological theories of ageing at both the macro level (evolutionary theories) and the micro level (cellular ageing). (*Questions 2.4 and 2.5*)

2.5   Review sociological and psychological theories of ageing. (*Question 2.6*)

Questions for Chapter 2

Question 2.1 (*Objective 2.2*)

Describe the type of older person who is statistically likely to be in poor health.

Question 2.2 (*Objectives 2.2 and 2.3*)

An older person is described to you as having 'difficulty getting around'. What are the possible causes of this?

Question 2.3 (*Objective 2.3*)

You are now told that the person in Question 2.2 has difficulty walking. Describe a range of different kinds of walking difficulties and how they arise.

Question 2.4 (*Objective 2.4*)

Explain why ageing is not considered to be a consequence of evolution by natural selection.

Question 2.5 (*Objectives 2.3 and 2.4*)

If you were offered a choice of the following products, which one would you choose and why? (You should consider the feasibility of developing such products.)

1   A rejuvenating skin cream.

2   An 'elixir of life' containing anti-oxidants.

3   A nerve tonic to prevent loss of memory.

4   A life-enhancing calorie-controlled diet plan.

5   An ointment to take the stiffness out of joints.

Question 2.6 (*Objective 2.5*)

What are the sociological factors and psychological characteristics which would be protective of health in old age?

References

Antonovsky, A. (1984) The sense of coherence as a determinant of health, in Matarazzo, J. P. (ed.) *Behavioural Health*, Wiley, New York.

de Beauvior, S. (1977) *Old Age*, Penguin Books, Harmondsworth.

Berkman, L. and Syme, S. (1979) Social networks, host resistance and mortality. A nine-year follow up of Alameda County residents, *American Journal of Epidemiology*, **109**, pp. 186–204.

Blakemore, K. and Boneham, M. (1993) *Age, Race and Ethnicity: A Comparative Approach*, Open University Press, Buckingham.

Brown, G. and Harris, T. (1978) *The Social Origins of Depression*, Tavistock, London.

Caplan, A. (1995) An improved future?, *Scientific American*, September, pp. 110-11.

Coleman, P. (1993) Adjustment in later life, in Bond, J. P., Coleman, P. and Peace, S. (eds) *Ageing in Society*, Sage, London.

Colerick, E. J. (1985) Stamina in later life, *Social Science and Medicine*, **21**(9), pp. 997–1006.

Cumming, E. and Henry, W. E. (1961) *Growing Old: The Process of Disengagement*, Basic Books, New York.

Davies, I., Johnson, J., Leeming, J and Sidell, M. (1994) *Our Bodies in Later Life*, Unit 7, K256 An Ageing Society, Open University, Milton Keynes.

Erikson, E. (1982) *The Life Cycle Completed: A Review*, Norton, New York.

Friedman, D. B. and Johnson, T. E. (1988) A mutation in the *age-1* gene in *Caenorhabditis elegans* lengthens life and reduces hermaphrodite fertility, *Genetics*, **118**, pp. 75–86.

Fries, J. F. and Crapo, L. M. (1981). *Vitality and Ageing: Implications of the Rectangular Curve*, Freeman and Co.

Havighurst, R. J. (1963) Successful ageing, in Williams, R. H. *et al.* (eds) *Processes of Ageing*, **1**, pp. 299–320, Atherton, New York.

Johnson, M. (1993) Dependency and interdependency, in Bond, J., Coleman, P. and Peace, S. (eds) *Ageing and Society*, 2nd edn, Sage, London.

Jung, C. G. (1933) *Modern Man in Search of a Soul*, Harcourt and Brace, New York.

Kobasa, S. C., Maddi, S. R. and Corrington, S. (1981) Personality and constitution as mediators in the stress-illness relationship, *Journal of Health and Social Behaviour*, **22**, pp. 368–78.

Kobasa, S. C., Maddi, S. R. and Kahn, S. (1982) Hardiness and health: A prospective study, *Journal of Personality and Social Psychology*, **42** (1), pp. 168–77.

Martin, G. M. (1978) Genetic syndromes in man with potential relevance to the pathobiology of ageing, *Birth Defects; Original Article Series*, **14**, pp. 5–39.

McGue, M., Vaupel, J. W., Holm, N. and Harvald, B. (1993) Longevity is moderately heritable in a sample of Danish twins, *Journal of Gerontology*, **48**(6), pp.237–44.

Moody, H. R. (1995) Ageing, meaning and the allocation of resources, *Ageing and Society*, **15**, pp. 163-84.

Olshansky, S. J., Caras, B. A. and Cassel, C. K. (1993) The ageing of the human species, *Scientific American*, **268**, no. 4, pp. 18-24.

Office of Population Censuses and Surveys (1988).

Scrutton, S. (1992) *Ageing, Health and in Control*, Chapman & Hall, London.

Slater, R. (1994) *Psychological Changes and Challenges in Later Life*, Unit 8 , K256 An Ageing Society, Open University, Milton Keynes.

Townsend, P. and Davidson, N. (eds) (1986) *Inequalities in Health: The Black Report*, Penguin, Harmondsworth.

Young, S. (1993) Against ageing, in *Mind and Body*, New Scientist supplement, April 17th, pp. 10–12.

CHAPTER 3
DEATH AND DYING:
BIOLOGICAL AND CULTURAL
CONTEXTS

3.1 Introduction

Dying and death are the end of the normal lifespan yet many people find discussing these topics difficult. However, the social and biological changes during the last stages of life are very important and are often retained as the most powerful memories of that person by their relatives and friends.

In the Western world for much of the first part of the 20th century, talking about death and dying, other than in children's stories and films, was seen as a taboo resembling the non-discussion of sex in Victorian times. It is noticeable that since the 1960s there have been increasing numbers of books written about death and dying. To some extent this counters the belief that Westerners don't like thinking about death, even though they don't talk about it very often. But some aspects of death and dying are still very much stereotyped in the wider population. Until someone close to you is dying, you may not have cause to contemplate some of the particular issues you will consider in this chapter.

3.2 Historical and cultural approaches to dying

Beliefs and approaches to death and dying have been moderated by cultural traditions and environmental conditions over time. Attitudes towards death have clearly been influenced by the range of demographic patterns of death and dying in different societies. Until the 19th century in the UK – and in some economically developing countries even today – few adults expected to live to old age, many women died in childbirth, and those who themselves survived seldom expected all their children to live beyond infancy.

3.2.1 Approaches of early societies

Archaeologists have uncovered a considerable range of details that inform us about the beliefs around death and the burial rites in early societies. The earliest known tombs date from the Middle Palaeolithic period and provide evidence that these people anticipated a continued existence after death.

Graves have been found dating around 50 000–60 000 years ago. Some were stacked with shells, bones and ivory ornaments with the body placed in a fetal position. At Shanidar Cave, in Iraq, a Neanderthal grave had been strewn with flowers. Most often Neanderthals (whose remains are not found to be more recent than 40 000 years old) buried tools and meat alongside their dead, a clear indication of an expectation of a further life where such accoutrements would be useful. This practice occurs in many later civilizations; for example, ancient Greece (Figure 3.1).

Figure 3.1   Terracotta objects found in a girl's grave (ancient Greece): a doll, a pair of tiny boots, and a thigh-guard (used by women in the preparation of wool).

One of the earliest written accounts of such beliefs can be found at Sakkarah, Egypt, in the Pyramid Texts. These date from about 4 000 years ago and offer two different views about the afterlife. In the first, the pharaohs were seen as children of the sun god, Atun-Re. At death they returned to their divine father and enjoyed eternal bliss with him. The second view of the afterlife was rather harsher. It was linked with a legendary hero, Osiris, who was believed to have risen from the dead. This was possible because his body had been preserved by embalming. He then presided over life in the West. It was believed that the West could be reached via passage over the river of death and through the underworld, where the deceased had to convince 42 assessors that they had not committed any of the 42 deadly sins. However, even successful negotiation of the underworld was only a prelude to the final judgement when a feather representing truth was weighed against the individual's heart (Figure 3.2 overleaf). To embark upon the journey toward eternal life, the body had to survive and therefore had to be embalmed. Although the Pyramid Texts focus on the destiny of the Egyptian leaders, they do suggest that any person rich enough to afford embalming and funeral rituals could also survive death. Thus in this period, the afterlife seemed accessible primarily through wealth and status (Figure 3.3). However, the texts also suggest, as in the weighing of the heart, that acts carried out in life might influence one's fate after death.

Figure 3.2   The weighing of the heart (ancient Egypt).

Inscriptions on later tombs constructed in the second millennium demonstrate that certain positive actions might lead to rewards. These actions include looking after the sick, poor and indigent, and refraining from bad behaviour. However, this idea of ultimate reward for a morally good life, an idea which has had considerable influence on Western societies, did not recur for many centuries.

Many early cultures did not have a universally positive attitude towards life after death. The Epic of Gilgamesh, a Mesopotamian text, contains a grim description of the dwelling place of the dead as the house of darkness – 'the house whose occupants are bereft of light; where dust is their food and clay their sustenance'. Yet immortality could be granted by the gods, and kings were buried along with their entire households who followed the royal corpse into the tomb, drank poison and died ready to serve their master in a new life.

Figure 3.3   Tomb of Tutankhamon with fresco and outer gold sarcophagus.

3.2.2 Approaches to death during the Christian era

The French philosopher Philippe Ariès pioneered studies of Western
attitudes toward death. Much of his research focused, inevitably, on
Christian practices; however, he notes the influences of pre-Christian
findings on later practices. He suggests that ancient funeral rituals (evident
from illustrations on tombs) aimed 'to prevent the deceased from *returning* to
disturb the living' (Ariès, 1974). To this end the dead were kept in sepulchres
or, as in Rome, buried in cemeteries outside the city limits, for example along
the Appian Way (Figure 3.4). However, by the sixth century, burials were
taking place within the church itself or in the grounds. Thereafter, for more
than a thousand years, cemeteries were used as a forum for socializing and
trading without creating discomfort. But by the middle of the 17th century,
texts suggest that people had become uncomfortable with the mix of sports
and markets which took place amongst the tombs, some of which smelt
unpleasantly when, for various reasons, they were opened.

Figure 3.4   Artist's reconstruction of a Roman funeral procession and burial ground.

Ariès suggests that until recent times death was familiar, and the living
accepted their own deaths in the same way as they happily incorporated the
ultimate resting places of the dead in their social lives. Burial was part of
daily functioning and took place alongside other social and business events.
Between the 12th and 15th centuries, three categories of images prevail: that
of death, that of the individual's knowledge of his or her own biography, and
that of an attachment to things and particular people. This renewed focus on
individualism can be illustrated by a new way of seeing the relationship
between acts on Earth and the judgement of God. Before that, collective
judgement was emphasized, with resurrection occurring only at the end of
history; this idea was replaced by the view that individuals were judged when
they died.

Till the end of the Middle Ages, the doctrine of purgatory had been central
to Christian views about death. The belief was that after death the soul went
to a temporary place of suffering and testing while the final destination,
heaven or hell, was decided. The ultimate fate could be influenced by the
actions and prayers of the living. This belief changed, however, once death
was seen as the point at which the soul's fate was determined. It then came to
be believed that only the behaviour of the individual was relevant, and so the
ties between the living and dead were changed.

With the approach of modernity, views about death and dying changed once more. Prior to the 20th century, most people died at home surrounded by their family, friends and neighbours. People were accustomed to death, insofar as they looked after dying relatives and friends, watched them die and, according to Ariès, were less afraid of death. He calls this 'tamed death'. While life expectancy in England during the Middle Ages is estimated to have been about 33 years, by the 19th century this had risen to 41 years, and now in the economically developed world it is approaching 80 years for women and almost 73 years for men. These changes in life expectancy, along with many other social and environmental differences as well as medical advances, have contributed to a diametrically opposed view of death, what Ariès calls 'forbidden death'. This sees communication about death as a lie, starting originally with the intention to spare the sick person from the knowledge about the imminence of death, to 'assume the burden of the ordeal', and then progressing to protecting society from the reality of death. This view is now challenged by the growth of organizations such as hospices to care for dying people, and many self-help and statutory organizations which focus on the needs of bereaved people. As we live longer, more of us are bereaved for longer periods and it becomes a greater problem for society to handle and, consequently, harder to ignore.

3.2.3 Approaches to death in a multi-cultural society

As noted above, historical attitudes towards death have changed in the Western Christian tradition over the centuries. But the UK is a multi-cultural society and has many citizens from different religious and cultural groups who have retained their belief systems and practices. Different cultures have particular attitudes towards life as well as death which influence their perceptions of the appropriate care of dying, deceased and bereaved people. For example, Judaism, Islam, Hinduism and Sikhism all emphasize the sacredness of life and contain clear directives that life should not be curtailed. This has a number of implications, ranging from the ways in which health workers might broach the question of pain and symptom control to the acceptability (or not) of suicide and euthanasia, to which we will return in later sections of this chapter.

Summary of Section 3.2

1   Views about death, dying and the afterlife have changed considerably over the centuries and are culturally mediated.

2   These views affect the way that dying people are cared for as well as how their bodies are treated after death.

3.3 Social attitudes towards death and dying people

The extent to which individuals have had control over their bodies and over death has depended primarily on the norms and dictates of the grouping with which that individual was associated. Even within groups, the psychological and emotional variations towards sustaining life or the value of life are considerable. Judaism and Islam believe that life is sacred and should not be prematurely terminated by others. In some societies, however, life is 'cheap', although we might see this as a Western and rather loaded value-judgement.

❑   Give an alternative explanation as to why some societies might not hold life to be sacred.

■   A belief in reincarnation of the individual might make death more acceptable, particularly if the hope is for a better existence next time around. Alternatively, an heroic or selfless belief in the needs of society will lead some people to sacrifice their lives for an ideal. For example, a pilot might stay at the controls of their plane to avoid crashing into an inhabited area.

Nevertheless, for some people life seems worthless or intolerable and they wish to see a way out, through suicide or euthanasia.

Euthanasia arouses considerable controversy. Some link both suicide and murder to euthanasia because in many traditions there is no concept of mercy killing. One country where euthanasia is tolerated under certain conditions, although technically illegal, is the Netherlands. Doctors are not prosecuted for ending patients' lives as long as it is clear that it was the patient's wish, and that a number of doctors had been consulted. In the USA, euthanasia is not accepted; however, in a number of states, citizens are encouraged while they are still healthy to complete 'living wills' which identify the measures they want, or do not want, to be carried out when they are unable to decide for themselves.

The Select Committee on Medical Ethics (1995), chaired by Lord Walton, chose to use the term *advance directive* instead of 'living will' to describe the document shown in Box 3.1. At the time of writing (1997), advance directives have some legal standing in the UK, although they are still being debated in a number of fora.

Box 3.1   An example of an advance directive, issued by the Voluntary Euthanasia Society

Advance directive

TO MY FAMILY, MY PHYSICIAN AND ALL OTHER PERSONS CONCERNED
THIS DIRECTIVE is made by me

_____

at a time when I am of sound mind and after careful consideration.

I DECLARE that if at any time the following circumstances exist, namely:

(1) I suffer from one or more of the conditions mentioned in the schedule; and

(2) I have become unable to participate effectively in decisions about my medical care; and

(3) two independent physicians (one a consultant) are of the opinion that I am unlikely to recover from illness or impairment involving severe distress or incapacity for rational existence.

THEN AND IN THOSE CIRCUMSTANCES my directions are as follows:

(1) that I am not to be subjected to any medical intervention or treatment aimed at prolonging or sustaining my life;

(2) that any distressing symptoms (including any caused by lack of food or fluid) are to be fully controlled by appropriate analgesic or other treatment, even though that treatment may shorten my life.

I consent to anything proposed to be done or omitted in compliance with the directions expressed above and absolve any medical attendants from any civil liability arising out of such acts or omissions.

I wish it to be understood that I fear degeneration and indignity far more than I fear death. I ask my medical attendants to bear this statement in mind when considering what my intentions would be in any uncertain situation.

I RESERVE the right to revoke this DIRECTIVE at any time, but unless I do so it should be taken to represent my continuing directions.

Schedule

(A)   Advanced disseminated malignant disease.

(B)   Severe immune deficiency.

(C)   Advanced degenerative disease of the nervous system.

(D)   Severe and lasting brain damage due to injury, stroke, disease or other cause.

(E)   Senile or pre-senile dementia, whether Alzheimer's, multi-infarct or other.

(F)   Any other condition of comparable gravity.

Signed _____ Date _____

WE TESTIFY that the above-named signed this Directive in our presence, and made it clear to us that he/she understood what it meant. We do not know of any pressure being brought on him/her to make such a directive and we believe it was made by his/her own wish. So far as we are aware we do not stand to gain from his/her death.

Witnessed by: _____

The term **social death** was coined in the 1960s by Glaser and Strauss (1965, 1968) and Sudnow (1967) to describe patients who were treated by others as if they were not there. These people might be young or old, but what they had in common was that those interacting with them regarded them as existing without social attributes. These important studies conducted in the USA highlighted the fate of many dying people who were seen to be neglected by their carers, particularly professional carers. They were isolated and the standard of their basic care, let alone pain control, was in many cases extremely poor. Subsequently, much attention was focused on why health care workers chose to ignore dying people in this way. It seemed that the quality of care given by these health workers depended on what they perceived to be the patient's awareness of their own condition.

The care given to patients can be affected by other kinds of social judgements. For example, studies in the USA have found that following traumatic incidents, certain categories of people are deemed to be worth resuscitating, others not. A middle-aged professional person is more likely to be given full attention in the emergency room of a hospital's casualty department than someone of low social status.

Some people, other than those who are biologically dying, are perceived to be socially dead. '**Pre-death** – physical life that continues stubbornly despite serious progressive mental disability' was described in the 1970s by the leading British geriatrician, Bernard Isaacs, and his colleagues (1971) when describing people with dementia. As a person with Alzheimer's or other types of neurodegenerative condition deteriorates, it becomes more and more difficult to identify their previous characteristics and engage with the pre-illness personality. Hence, many people find their demented relatives hard to recognize and relate to, and grieve for them long before they are biologically dead.

Summary of Section 3.3

1   In many societies we see a reluctance to allow individuals the right to choose to die.

2   Yet, even in the same society, people who are dying and others who are demented may be treated as though already dead, hence the use of the terms *social death* and *pre-death*.

3.4 Caring for the dying person

The medicalization of death and dying, which began in the early part of the 20th century, meant that dying people were progressively removed from the home into a hospital or another institutional setting. The first research studies investigating the fate of dying people were undertaken in the 1960s and demonstrated the extent to which dying people were isolated from other patients in hospitals. Indeed, they suffered from what might now be seen as medical neglect. Many people dying from cancer were reported to suffer intractable pain and excruciating symptoms. It has already been mentioned that the studies by Sudnow and by Glaser and Strauss identified that some of the problems faced by dying people were a consequence of the attitudes of their professional carers. For many physicians, dying patients were constant reminders of the limitations of medicine, and one often-used coping mechanism was to 'write them off'. It remains true that some consultants find a dying patient to be an embarrassment and don't really know how to talk to them, let alone how to treat them.

However, the rise of the hospice movement in the 1970s brought to public notice the fate of dying people in a variety of settings. Dame Cecily Saunders, the founder of the modern hospice movement, introduced the concept of an holistic approach to caring for dying people. The dying person became central to their own planned care regime, rather than being seen as one of medicine's failures. Sustaining relatively healthy living while dying was defined in the broadest sense to include emotional and spiritual well-being. The aim of the palliative care movement was to achieve this goal.

3.4.1 Palliative care

The World Health Organisation (WHO) defines **palliative care** as:

> *the care of patients with active progressive, far advanced disease and a limited prognosis and for whom the focus of care is the quality of life.*
>
> **Palliation** *is the relief of suffering and palliative care is concerned with the effects and symptoms of a disease rather than the pathology itself.*

The palliative care and hospice movements have developed a philosophy based on a multidisciplinary approach which focuses primarily on *living while dying*. The dying person is central to a multiprofessional team working to ensure that appropriate care is available but also enabling (as far as possible) the dying person to maintain control and choice about all aspects of that care. In addition, the team strives to ensure that carers – especially informal carers – get adequate attention and support to enable them to cope with the crisis at hand. The national network of hospice and palliative care workers provides a hands-on advice service to primary health care workers as well as hospital workers, to support them in enabling dying people to retain a reasonable quality of life while dying.

Although most people still actually die in hospital, much of the terminal period is spent in the dying person's own home with care provided by the family supported by the primary health care team. The decision to admit a dying person to hospital will usually be taken because it has become impossible to care for them at home or because the dying person is suffering from acute pain or other symptoms.

Pain relief and symptom control are central to sustaining the quality of life while dying. The hospice and palliative care movements have emphasized the rights of people to live while dying and to receive relief for whatever symptoms or pain they are experiencing. The hospice philosophy identifies not only physical pain, but also spiritual, psychological and emotional pain. However, the hospice model of addressing pain is derived from experience of people suffering from pain caused by cancer and (to a lesser extent) those with motor neurone disease and AIDS. This explains why the following section exploring pain relief methods focuses almost exclusively on addressing pain resulting from malignancies. Palliative care specialists maintain that the principles of pain control and symptom relief are the same for the care of people who are dying from other diseases, and indeed for the care of those suffering non-terminal chronic pain.

3.4.2 Pain relief and symptom control

The hospice movement, in focusing on pain relief for people with cancer, has pioneered pharmacological preparations to enable dying people to remain conscious, in control and relatively pain- and symptom-free. If pain is properly assessed and treated it is very rare for it to be intractable. However, many people are still concerned about the effects of taking addictive drugs such as heroin for pain control.

❑   Is there evidence that morphine is addictive when given for pain relief?

◼   No. The evidence is that those given morphine for pain relief do not become drug addicts; that is, they do not become *psychologically* dependent on morphine (Book 4, Chapter 4).

❑   What other reason is given for limiting the dose level of morphine?

◼   The concern that the patient will develop tolerance and need larger and larger doses for the analgesic to be effective.

❑   Is this view justified?

◼   No. Melzack quotes studies showing that morphine can be administered for months or even years without the patient developing tolerance (Book 4, Chapter 4).

It is certainly the case that the body will very likely develop *physical* addiction which is to say that sudden withdrawal of a drug would cause unpleasant physical side-effects. However, in the event of recovery, provided the patient is gradually weaned off the drug, this will not be a problem. So there is no reason to withhold morphine from the dying person in pain. Ideally, the dosage is adjusted so that, once pain has occurred, it is thereafter treated so that it is always kept in abeyance.

Most people find it easiest to take drugs orally, but a weak patient or one who has difficulty swallowing may need to use a suppository or to use some other method. Certain drugs can be delivered on a 24-hour basis, subcutaneously through a syringe driver, enabling dying people to administer these themselves while at home.

❏   What approach other than drug use can suppress pain?

▓   Stimulation of large-diameter nerve fibres (Book 4, Chapter 4).

This is achieved by the use of small boxes consisting of a battery-powered stimulator connected to electrodes which are placed on the skin. The technique is know as TENS (transcutaneous electrical nerve stimulation; see Book 4, Chapter 2, for its use in control of pain in labour). Only about 30% of those with chronic pain find TENS useful, but for these people it offers an easily controlled method of pain relief. The intensity of the stimulus pulse is under their control. When the appropriate level is found, 15–30 minutes treatment can abolish pain for many hours.

3.4.3 Establishing the cause of pain

Before starting any treatment for pain relief it is necessary to gather a considerable amount of information. This is because establishing the precise cause of the pain can be quite difficult.

❏   Why do you think establishing the cause of pain can present difficulties?

▓   Establishing the cause of the pain can be difficult because there are two dimensions to unravelling the perception of pain, the physical and the emotional. On the one hand it may not be straightforward to locate the site of actual tissue damage; for example, consider the implications of phenomena such as referred pain or phantom limb pain for the physician who is trying to arrive at a diagnosis. On the other hand, there is clearly an emotional dimension to pain that must be resolved (Book 4, Chapter 4).

Many people with advanced malignant disease have pain at more than one site and careful assessment is required. The doctor might ask the following:

1   Where do you feel the pain?

2   Describe your pain and tell me how bad it is.

3   When did you first notice the pain?

4   Is there anything that makes your pain feel better or worse?

'Where do you feel the pain?'

Referred pain may be confusing to the sufferer: 'Why does my doctor think I've got a heart problem when it's my left arm and shoulder that are painful?' However, the shared neuronal pathways to the brain are known so, having first established that there is nothing wrong with the arm or shoulder, the physician can make a diagnosis of angina as the likely source of the pain.

Figure 3.5 The body shown divided into dermatomes (right) and the corresponding segmentation of the spinal cord (below). For instance, the dermatome T12 corresponds to an area around the waist; sensory information arising here will enter the spinal cord in the nerve marked T12 in the lower part of the figure. Co, S, L, T and C refer to the coccygeal (tail), sacral (hip), lumbar (lower back), thoracic (chest) and cervical (neck) regions of the spinal cord respectively.

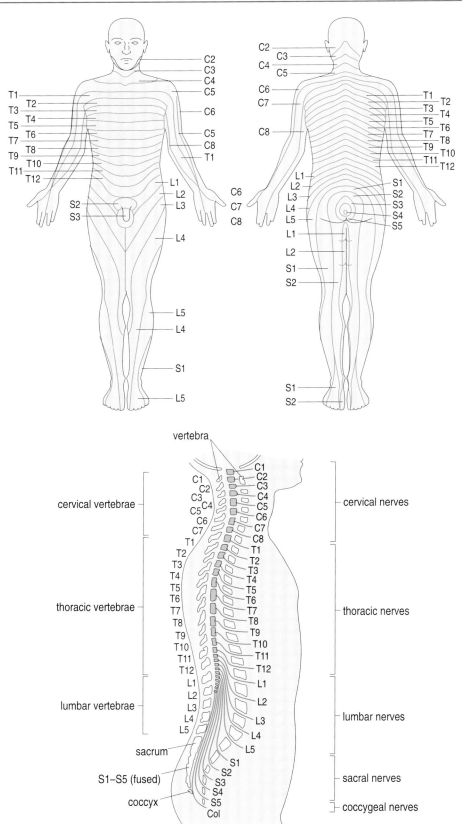

❏   From Figures 3.5, can you suggest the site of a pain that is felt in the
       area of the dermatome around the umbilicus (belly button)?

■   The area of tissue damage may well be the gut (in particular the region
       of the appendix). Another possibility is that the pain arises from
       pressure on the nerve itself. Pain caused by a spinal bone (vertebra)
       collapsing and pressing on a nerve root is felt in the bone itself (local
       site) and over the area of skin served by that nerve – the dermatome
       (Book 2, Chapter 3).

Another classic diagnosis is that a deep-seated central abdominal pain which
radiates through to the back is highly suggestive of damage arising in the
pancreas.

'Describe your pain and tell me how bad it is'

The type and severity of the pain can often indicate its source. Nerve pain is
described as burning or shooting and is particularly unpleasant. Nerve
compression often leads to a deep ache, while nerve destruction may be
associated with areas of numbness and abnormal sensation and can be very
severe. Bone pain is typically described as aching or gnawing. Although
initially it may be intermittent, eventually it can become continuous and
relentless.

'When did you first notice the pain?'

It is important to know if any events were associated with the onset of the
pain since they may be relevant when coming to a diagnosis. Sudden onset of
severe sharp pain localized to a particular bony area might, for example,
indicate local fracture. But pain can also be a side-effect of treatment. For
example, pain in the upper abdomen which coincided with starting an anti-
inflammatory drug is likely to be due to gastritis caused by that drug.
Gastritis is an inflammation of the stomach mucosa. Many older people
suffer constantly from mild gastritis. Taking a drug such as aspirin that itself
irritates the cells of the mucosa before being absorbed, can actually
exacerbate the symptoms in the upper abdomen even though a reduction in
the inflammatory reaction may be achieved elsewhere.

'Is there anything that makes your pain feel better or worse?'

From the above it is clear that it is necessary to monitor treatment. In the
first instance, though, it may be possible to derive information about the
nature of the damage by asking whether any factor (activity, diet, time of
day) seems to affect the level of pain experienced. For example, cancerous
tissue in the pelvic bones or thigh bones often only causes pain when bearing
weight.

An example: alleviating bone pain

From the answers to these four questions the physician might be able to pinpoint the area of damage responsible for the pain. The exact nature of the damage might need further investigation. For example, there are several mechanisms, any one of which may result in the experience of bone pain. Local destruction of bone or the presence of areas of abnormally dense bone may cause pain. If there is a malignancy, the cancer cells may destroy bone directly or initiate damage by producing chemicals which activate bone cells causing an increase either in the normal re-absorption of bone (osteolysis) or in the laying down of bone (osteosclerosis).

❑   What are the names of these bone cells?

◼   Osteoclasts are the phagocytic cells that destroy bone. Osteoblasts produce collagen, which together with mineral salts form the matrix of bone (Book 2, Chapter 2).

Early confirmation of a diagnosis is essential. In the case of bone pain it might include a bone scan to ascertain the type of damage and detect local spread. However, for some dying people the experience of a scan can be quite distressing and the decision to use it needs to incorporate an understanding of the upheaval and discomfort a scan may create, particularly for a bedridden person or wheelchair user. On the other hand, failure to diagnose and treat bone cancer can lead to the collapse of the vertebral column, compression of the spinal cord and hence lower limb paralysis. X-rays could indicate the likelihood of imminent fracture in a long bone. Such information is important for the dying person who might be advised to reduce weight-bearing on a fragile bone.

So what can be done about bone pain to reduce discomfort and raise the dying person's quality of life?

In most cases, it is possible to modify pain through analgesia. In addition, metal pins or plates surgically inserted may reduce discomfort, but this is not always possible with very ill patients or in cases where the bone itself could not sustain the attachment of a device. Especially where pain is hard to treat, it is important to set realistic goals such as freedom from pain at night and at rest, even if this is not possible when the person is mobile. The use of a wheelchair may help and partially restore the dying person's confidence and independence.

3.4.4 The perception of pain

When assessing how to treat a dying person, it is essential to establish that individual's perception of the importance of a particular pain. The dying person may feel that his or her quality of living is more inconvenienced or compromised by a relatively non-life-threatening pain such as toothache or a condition such as flatulence.

Usually, a first step towards treating mild pain would be the use of non-opioids such as paracetamol. As the pain becomes worse, weak opioids or codeine preparations will be appropriate. Once the pain is very severe, strong opioids such as morphine or diamorphine should be considered. Oral analgesics are usually the first route but when these are no longer effective other routes are explored.

❑   Give examples of these other methods.

■   The syringe driver delivers the analgesia subcutaneously. A suppository offers analgesia via anal insertion.

Other physical causes of pain and discomfort should be considered, bearing in mind the pharmacological effects of many strong painkillers. For example, constipation is a known side-effect of MST, a morphine-based painkiller used to combat severe cancer pain. As constipation can in itself be just as painful as the malignancies, prophylactic treatment should be given before the problem arises.

3.4.5 The concept of 'total pain'

In addition to pain and problems caused by medication, dying people suffer a range of other symptoms that affect their quality of life and may cause distress. These include breathlessness, weakness, gastrointestinal symptoms such as nausea and vomiting, and neurological symptoms such as confusion. It is important to talk about these symptoms with the patient, their relatives and carers. Wherever possible, one should explain them and allay unnecessary fears.

Pain is not a simple sensation but a complex physiological and emotional experience (Regnard and Davies, 1986). The way in which the different dimensions of pain summate to give the totality of the experience can be diagrammatically represented as shown in Figure 3.6.

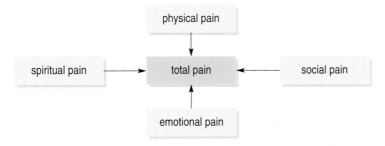

Figure 3.6   The concept of 'total pain'.

❑   In what ways would breathlessness contribute to 'total pain'?

■   There may be physical pain in the throat and chest. It also contributes to emotional pain when it induces fear in the sufferer.

Emotional pain can be generated by a number of emotions.

❑   Which emotions do you think will contribute to the experience of pain?

■   Sadness, depression, disappointment, fear, sense of loss, despair, anger, anxiety, grief, denial are the emotions we thought of; you may have added others to this list.

Social pain describes the feelings that are generated by the different kinds of social isolation; these range from actually being alone to simply feeling cut off, ignored or unable to communicate effectively, perhaps because of a sense of embarrassment about discussing issues around the approach of death. Financial problems are generally grouped with social factors and believed to cause social pain; you may agree with this, or you may feel that they would more likely lead to emotional pain. There are no hard and fast rules here, but the concept of 'total pain' can help palliative care workers to ensure that they treat the patient holistically.

Summary of Section 3.4

1   The growth of the hospice and palliative care movement have focused particularly on enabling people to retain a reasonable quality of life whilst dying.

2   Although most people still die in hospitals, the principles embodied by palliative care are now filtering through into many settings.

3   Hence, regardless of the site of caring for the dying person, there is now increased access to specialist care which includes pain relief and symptom control.

4   In caring for dying people, palliative care specialists explore what they describe as 'total pain', which includes emotional, spiritual, social as well as physical pain.

3.5 Nearing death

The significance of dying varies among people; some might welcome death as a release from a disease-racked body and dependence on others, or see it as the welcome reunion with those who have died before. Most people who know they are terminally ill, experience some psychological, emotional or spiritual distress.

3.5.1 Facing the fear of death

For some people, acknowledging that death is imminent is intolerable and hence attempts to raise this subject may be counterproductive. However, many dying people experience considerable distress about the uncertainty of their fate and the impact their death will have on their survivors. Hence, when the subject is raised by palliative care workers, it might release dying people from some of their anxieties and enable them to talk about their feelings. It may subsequently be possible to talk about their feelings with those most important to them.

Many elderly people today live for a long time with an increasingly frail body. They too have hopes and fears about their death but all too often there is no-one willing or able to talk this through with them. The taboo mentioned at the beginning of this chapter operates strongly here. This can make it difficult for the dying person who has accepted their future to gain 'permission' to go. Too often they receive hearty encouragement to 'soldier on'.

Everyone fears the unknown and for this reason death is probably universally feared. No-one can tell us what our death will be like, but like our birth (unremembered by us but experienced differently by our mothers) it will be unique.

Some of our fears could be allayed by more information. This can come from a variety of organizations who arrange seminars and workshops. It is also comforting to discover that a physician in the 19th century who chronicled the death of his patients reported that the majority slipped away silently (and see Box 3.2 for an 18th-century account). This seems a surprising observation for a period when medicine was less sophisticated and more younger people died from disease. Maybe our ancestors were more generous with the opium? The custom of visiting and sitting with dying people may also have helped in this respect.

These descriptions, and others, of sitting quietly holding the hand of a loved one who dies so gently that the exact moment of death is undiscerned are at odds with tales of death agonies and the death rattle. But we shall see in Section 3.7 that these happen when death occurs and only under certain conditions.

Box 3.2   The death of William East (1759)

William East was a colourful itinerant music teacher from Waltham in Leicestershire. The following eyewitness account of his death appears in *The Spiritual Gamut*, a religious tract published shortly after East's death in 1759.

For about a week before his death, his spirit seemed somewhat dull. He had no rapturous flame, or sudden flashes of joy, which he expected he should have been continually filled with. Notwithstanding he seemed to enjoy a sweet composure of mind ... And now, ... when the great messenger of mortality came, he looked upon him without any visible appearance of horror ... He called his children to him, kissed them and took his leave of them, and then flung himself into the bosom of his wife and quietly fell asleep.'

3.5.2 The influence of cultural and religious traditions

In some cases the cultural and religious tradition of the dying person will influence the way in which he or she perceives the dying process.

The French philosopher Michel de Montaigne wrote that the utility of living consisted not in the length of days, but in the use of time: 'L'utilité du vivre n'est pas en l'espace, elle est en l'usage; tel a vécu longtemps qui a peu vécu' (a man may have lived long, and yet but a little). It is this thought that haunts many people as they age. The measure of the usefulness of their days tends to be influenced enormously by cultural expectations and refined by the perceived expectations of family and friends. Spiritual values, often coupled to the belief in an afterlife, may come to the fore in later years. Especially where these ideas have lain dormant for long periods, there may be concern that one's performance will fail to 'make the grade' in the eyes of the deity. For others, the whole of life has been spent unobtrusively making spiritual preparation for death. Then it is possible to greet death cheerfully, assured of a greater peace and joyfulness to come. Hence a strong faith can sometimes override the fear and pain of death. On the other hand, spiritual pain can exacerbate the distress of a dying person, and sensitivity to these issues is essential to maintain trust as well as to improve the quality of life for the dying person throughout the terminal period, but particularly as death nears.

It is sometimes very clear to carers from a number of signs that death is imminent. Professional carers would hopefully have planned a range of scenarios in advance, possibly with the input of the dying person. Sometimes the end comes unexpectedly and hurried arrangements need to be made.

The needs of the dying person and the family are paramount. These may include enabling families to carry out specific cultural or religious practices. These may vary even within religions. For example, Hinduism is a culture as much as a religion, and the many variations in practices and ranges of belief depend on the language, regional origin, caste affiliation and sect of its followers. The caste system pervades the practices of Hinduism, influences many aspects of social behaviour, and has led to different interpretations of many of the laws of diet, prayer and ritual purification. Hindus have clear concepts of good and bad deaths. If the family perceive the death to be a bad one, signified by pain, vomit or the passing of faeces, they will attribute this to bad 'karma' and may be distressed. A good death is a conscious, willing, and peaceful one in old age, and is indicated by a peaceful facial expression, with a slightly open mouth or eyes. Some Hindus prepare themselves for a good death through fasting, partly for spiritual reasons and also to reduce the amount of bodily excretions at death.

Many Christians express a wish to receive communion or hear mass before they die. Non-Christian religious traditions place great importance on company for the dying person, and particularly that of relatives and friends to pray with or for them and to ensure that the appropriate rituals are carried out. This applies to Muslims and Jews as well as to Hindus and Sikhs. A dying Muslim would try to recite the Islamic declaration of faith (Shahada): 'I bear witness that there is no God but God, and Muhammad is His Messenger' and might want to face Mecca. Hindus and Sikhs attribute great significance to the deceased's last words as these may indicate his or her state of mind, and give some consolation to those left behind. Many Hindus and Sikhs believe that the soul is released more easily if the dying person is on the floor with his or her head facing north. The consequences of the distress caused by preventing the family from placing the dying Hindu on the floor could be life-long for the bereaved relatives.

Summary of Section 3.5

1   Death is feared by most people and, as it nears, being able to talk about it and ask questions may be helpful.

2   The approach of death is a time when religious and cultural beliefs and rituals are important.

3   Those who work in institutions need to recognize and familiarize themselves with the range and diversity of custom and practice so they can act as facilitators at the end.

3.6 Causes of death and the biological processes in dying

Death can occur at any age but, as previously explained, the likelihood of it occurring before the age of 40 has decreased dramatically over the 20th century for those living in Western societies. Older people in these societies tend to suffer from at least one of the following disease categories: atherosclerosis, hypertension, adult-onset diabetes mellitus, obesity, malignancies, or conditions of mental deterioration such as Alzheimer's and other dementias. These may not, of themselves, be the immediate cause of death although they may constitute predisposing factors. Yet in Western societies all deaths are categorized by cause, and 'old age' is not deemed to be a sufficiently informative description for a modern death certificate. For some people this obsession with medical causes of death seems to be an undignified way to proceed. It is no longer acceptable to die just of old age. In his best-selling book *How We Die* (Newland, 1993), the American physician Sherwin Newland writes: 'The government statisticians and scientific clinicians insist that proper names be applied to sluggish circulation and an antique heart'.

Indeed, according to death certificates, most elderly people in Western societies die of cardiovascular complications (Book 3, Chapter 2) so we might expect to find that, for example, the heart functions less well as we age. Figure 3.7 shows that this is so, at least as reflected by a decline in cardiac output (measured here as amount of blood pumped by the heart in one minute). Notice that the decline is represented as the function remaining expressed as a percentage of the function that was available at 30 years of age.

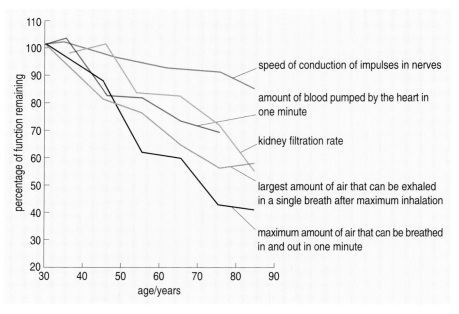

Figure 3.7   Decline in capacity of some organs in humans with increasing age.

❏   Use Figure 3.7 to compare the amount of blood pumped by the heart in 1 minute and the maximum amount of air that can be breathed in and out in a minute in a 70-year-old.

▪   The 70-year-old is pumping blood with about 70% of the efficiency of a 30-year-old, but the maximum amount of air that can be breathed in and out has been halved compared to that of the 30-year-old.

❏   Does this mean that the lungs are closer to the point where they will fail to meet the needs of the body than is the heart?

▪   Not necessarily. There are a number of points to consider, such as how much reserve capacity (Book 3, Chapter 2) there was at 30 years of age. In other words, the average 30-year-old may well have a heart and lungs that have outputs that are way in excess of normal day-to-day needs.

Consider first the lungs. In Book 3, Chapter 2, the tidal volume (the amount of air normally breathed in and out) is shown to be only about one-seventh in men (about 14%) and one-fifth in women (20%) of the maximum intake possible in forced inspiration and about one-third (33%) of the amount possible in forced expiration. So, provided that the respiratory surfaces are functioning normally, a 50% drop in reserve capacity as seen by 70 years of age still leaves the lungs a long way from failing to provide an adequate service for most day-to-day activity (although the potential for athletic performance is much diminished). In other words, the lungs have no problem in providing the tidal volume so far as we can judge from Figure 3.7. The question remains as to why there has been any loss at all.

❏   What suggestions can you make to account for the reduced ability to fill and empty the lungs in forced breathing?

■   You might have remembered from the previous chapter that there is often less flexibility in the costal cartilage and that this means that rib movements are restricted and hence forced breathing is less effective. Also the lungs contain a lot of collagen fibres, and, as you know, this protein loses its elasticity with age.

Turning now to the heart, Figure 3.7 shows the cardiac output, and you might recall that the resting output can double at times of anxiety or excitement (Book 3, Chapter 2; see also Table 3.1 below).

Table 3.1   Effect of various conditions on cardiac output. Approximate percentage changes are shown in parentheses.

Condition or factor	Effect
sleep	no change
moderate changes in environmental temperature	no change
anxiety and excitement	increase (50–100%)
eating	increase (30%)
exercise	increase (up to 70%)
high environmental temperature	increase
sitting or standing from lying position	decrease (20–30%)
rapid arrhythmia (heart beating irregularly)	decrease
heart disease	decrease

Even this does not take the heart's pumping capability anywhere near its limit, as it is estimated that the pumping capability is up to 400% above that normally required by the body.

❏   Figure 3.7 shows a drop of 30% by age 70. What reserve does this suggest?

■   The fall in reserve capacity is 30% of 400% which is:

$$400 \times \frac{30}{100} = \frac{12\,000}{100}$$

$$= 120\%$$

This leaves $400 - 120 = 280\%$.

So even by 70 years of age there is a reserve of 280%. Thus, even at times of excitement or anxiety, the aged heart should be able to maintain a sufficient cardiac output to meet the body's needs.

So the drop in reserves with age, as shown in Figure 3.7, does not suggest that the normal ageing processes push the body over that line from life to death. Why then should cardiovascular complications be one of the most common causes of death in the elderly when the aged heart has such a good cardiac output reserve?

3.6.1 Death and the cardiovascular system

Throughout the previous section we were describing healthy ageing organs. Unfortunately most older people in the Western world do not have healthy cardiovascular systems. For example, by the age of 60, about 75% of men and 25% of women have significant narrowing of the coronary arteries. (Recall from Book 3, Chapter 2, that this is caused by the build-up of lipids in the artery walls, and that it can develop into the pathological condition of atherosclerosis, when the lipids combine with calcium and cell debris to form *plaques* – not to be confused with the plaque that forms on your teeth!)

❑   Which organ do the coronary arteries supply?

▦   The heart; the coronary arteries branch off the aorta as the aorta leaves the heart.

Heart problems

It is somewhat sobering to discover that at least half the population do not have normal heart function, at an age which most of us do not regard as very old. As the blood supply to the heart muscle decreases, the risk of ischaemic heart disease increases and with it the risk of a heart attack or myocardial infarction (Book 3, Chapter 2). Studies have shown that there are also age-related changes in blood vessels; as the tissues age, the protein elastin becomes less elastic and hence the vessel walls become less supple and are described as being less *compliant*. This means that a greater pressure has to be exerted by the heart to pump blood through the vessels. Consequently, the heart requires more oxygen and other nutrients to do this work. These are resources that are supplied by the coronary artery, the very artery that we noted as being narrower in such a high proportion of the population.

❑   In Book 3, Chapter 2, it was explained that a heart attack does not inevitably cause death. Look at Figure 3.8, which shows the coronary arteries supplying the heart, and decide which of the two sites, labelled 1 and 2, is most likely, if blocked, to be responsible for a total cardiac arrest and death.

▦   Site 2, because the extent of heart muscle affected is greatest.

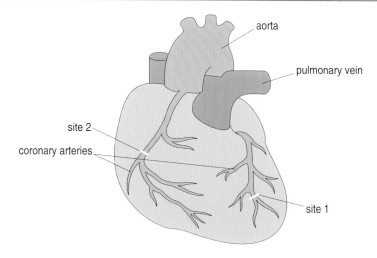

Figure 3.8   Coronary arteries supplying the heart.

Heart cells do not divide or regenerate so although the individual may functionally recover completely from a small heart attack the heart has been weakened. Similarly, lost neurons are not replaced and so any degeneration in the nerves that supply the sinoatrial node (SAN) results in loss of cells in the SAN itself and also in the bundle of His (Book 3, Chapter 2). This can result in the ventricular rhythm 'breaking free' from the normal 'whole heart' rhythm, and subsequent loss of coordination of the heartbeats. This need not, of itself, be life-threatening in our modern society as an artificial electrical pacemaker can be implanted beneath the skin with its electrodes connected to the right ventricle to restore the coordinated beating of the heart.

Strokes

The heart is not the only organ to be affected by less-efficient functioning of the cardiovascular system resulting from atherosclerosis. Other organs may also fail slowly as cells are intermittently starved of oxygen and glucose because the vascular system, with its less compliant vessels, fails to respond with sufficient speed to changing oxygen demands. When the organ affected is the brain, the incident is termed a *stroke* (Book 3, Chapter 2). A stroke can be brought about by the rupture of a vessel as well as by a clot forming in a vessel; in both instances the effects will be the same, namely the death of cells from oxygen starvation. One-quarter of strokes are caused by intracerebral bleeding (i.e. bleeding within the cerebral hemispheres), and these are the ones that are most likely to lead to immediate death.

Hypertension, diabetes and obesity

Atherosclerosis is the most common problem associated with coronary heart disease, and in Book 3, Chapter 2, a number of major risk factors causally linked to the onset of atherosclerosis were given. These included hypertension, diabetes mellitus and obesity.

❑   What do these three conditions have in common?

■   They are all conditions that tend to be suffered by older people in Western societies. (See the beginning of this section on the causes of death.)

❑   In what ways do each of these conditions place added burdens on the cardiovascular system?

■   Hypertension increases the blood pressure, therefore increasing the amount of work the heart has to do.

The form of diabetes mellitus that affects individuals from late middle age onward is known as non-insulin-dependent diabetes mellitus (NIDDM; Book 3, Chapter 4). Increased blood glucose levels occur as a consequence of the ineffectiveness of insulin. This has a dehydrating effect on tissues (water moves out in response to the increased osmotic pressure; Book 3 Chapter 5). The increased loss of glucose in the urine alters the osmotic pressure in the renal tubules and decreases tubular reabsorption of fluid. This can reduce the blood volume, resulting in an inadequate blood flow to tissues. Therefore the heart has to work harder to provide the cells with adequate resources. In addition, many people with NIDDM have atherosclerosis as a result of years of high levels of circulating lipids.

The kinds of problems associated with NIDDM can be a consequence of obesity as it too reduces the effectiveness of insulin. This comes about because the obese individual has a decreasing number of insulin receptors in the insulin target cells. It is observed that NIDDM and obesity are often associated (Book 3, Chapter 4).

Additionally, the obese tend to have a high-fat diet that leads to fatty deposits accumulating in arterial walls. These attract calcium and other cellular debris to form the plaques typical of atherosclerosis.

So we see that, with the exception of the dementias and malignancies, all the other disease categories mentioned at the beginning of the section on the causes of death can work in a synergistic way to make coronary heart disease likely to be described as the major cause of death in the elderly.

Equally, it is fair to say that any incompetence of the cardiovascular system has far-reaching implications for all other systems because in the end most deaths are caused by the destruction of tissues resultant upon an inadequate nutrient supply and failed waste disposal system. And so, in one sense, the body dies, bit by bit, without the individual noticing. Because of the way that the body functions as a whole with interdependence of all systems, this destruction can be 'blamed' on the circulatory system that has in the final analysis 'let down' the other organs – hence the rationale for the immediate cause of death, as described on the death certificate, being given as cardiovascular failure.

3.6.2 Edging towards death

Cardiovascular failure results in an insufficient blood flow to the tissues. This is termed **cardiovascular shock**. Shock is not exclusively a consequence of heart attacks; it may also be caused by haemorrhage, for example.

❏   Why would haemorrhage cause shock?

■   Loss of blood volume would cause a drop in blood pressure and hence a decrease in rate of blood supply to all tissues. The body is described as being in shock when, for any reason, blood supply drops to a level where tissue damage occurs.

❏   In what ways would reduced blood flow damage cells?

■   Reduced blood flow would result in an inadequate supply of substances such as oxygen and glucose and an accumulation of waste products because the sluggish circulation would remove them only slowly.

Thus the inefficiencies of an aged and damaged cardiovascular system lead to tissue damage that eventually becomes terminal just as surely as it does when there has been the sudden ceasing of heartbeat after an acute attack. In both cases the balance between intracellular and extracellular fluid is thrown out of kilter.

In fact the more we understand of the necessary interactions between the body's various control systems and the narrowness of the normal range within which the constituents of the intracellular fluid, and consequently the extracellular fluid, must be maintained, the more amazing it seems that life exists at all. Table 3.2 shows some of the important constituents and physical characteristics of extracellular fluid and their normal range of values. Values outside these tend to lead quite rapidly to death.

Table 3.2 Some important constituents and physical characteristics of the extracellular fluid, the normal range of control, and the approximate non-lethal limits for short periods. (Oxygen and carbon dioxide values are partial pressures in mmHg; the units of the other constituents listed are millimoles per litre.)

	Normal value	Normal range	Approximate non-lethal limits
oxygen	40	35–45	10–1000
carbon dioxide	40	35–45	5–80
sodium ion	142	138–146	115–175
potassium ion	4.2	3.8–5.0	1.5–9.0
calcium ion	1.2	1.0–1.4	0.5–2.0
chloride ion	108	103–112	70–130
bicarbonate ion	28	24–32	8–45
glucose	85	75–95	20–1500
body temperature	37.0 °C	37.0 °C	18.3–43.3 °C
pH	7.4	7.3–7.5	6.9–8.0

❑   Which physical characteristic is least tolerant to fluctuations?

▨   It is the pH of the extracellular fluid. The normal value of 7.4 can only drift by about 0.5 in either direction without fatal consequences.

❑   Which organ is responsible for regulating pH values?

▨   This is a function of the kidney (Book 3, Chapter 5).

You may recall that pH is a measure of hydrogen ion concentration or acidity (decrease in pH). A rise in acidity is prevented by hydrogen ions attaching to bicarbonate ions. The hydrogen ions are thereby neutralized and are held in this state until they can be excreted by the kidney. But the services of the circulatory system are required to transport this buffered fluid to the kidney.

Hydrogen ions are produced in metabolic processes, especially cellular respiration, and the bicarbonate ions are derived from carbon dioxide and water via the formation of carbonic acid and its subsequent dissociation, as shown below:

$$CO_2 \quad + \quad H_2O \rightleftharpoons H_2CO_3 \rightleftharpoons HCO_3^- \quad + \quad H^+$$

carbon   water   carbonic   bicarbonate   hydrogen
dioxide   acid   ions   ions

The malfunctioning of another system can lead to clinical abnormalities of the pH regulation.

❑   Looking at the equation above, which other system would you suppose to be important in the regulation of hydrogen ion concentration?

■   The concentration of carbon dioxide in the extracellular fluid is influenced by the rate of pulmonary ventilation, so it seems likely that the respiratory system is involved.

In fact, if the rate of pulmonary ventilation is decreased, the concentration of carbon dioxide in the extracellular fluid increases. This pushes the equation on p. 76 to the right and so increases the hydrogen ion concentration. The acidity of the fluid rises and this is expressed as a decreased pH value. The condition is known as *respiratory acidosis*.

❏   How could you deliberately achieve respiratory acidosis?

■   By holding your breath.

Holding your breath reduces pulmonary ventilation, so the exchange of respiratory gases is slowed down, but carbon dioxide will still be produced at a more-or-less constant rate from cellular respiration and so its level in the plasma and in the extracellular fluid rises. Provided your respiratory centre in the medulla is intact you will not be able to hold your breath for long enough to cause damage. Nevertheless the pH drops to a dangerous 7.0 before you are forced to take a breath.

There are a number of pathologies that can cause respiratory acidosis; essentially it will be caused by any factor that blocks the airways or reduces the efficiency of gas exchange in the lungs. Hence, respiratory infections such as bronchitis and pneumonia – 'the old person's friend' – can affect extracellular pH by this mechanism.

The respiratory centre in the medulla will act to attempt to increase ventilation whenever a rise in extracellular carbon dioxide is detected, irrespective of the cause responsible for this state. As mentioned above, in many pathologies, respiratory insufficiency (the inability to get rid of waste carbon dioxide) is *not* caused by lack of inspired oxygen but by some abnormality in the exchange of gases across the pulmonary membrane or by failure in oxygen transport from the lungs to other tissues. So increasing inspiration does not alleviate the situation. The feeling that this condition engenders can be one of panic or mental anguish. It is often described as 'air hunger' although the technical term is *dyspnoea*. Some people may seem to be fighting for breath as their life ebbs away. This is clearly unacceptable and proper diagnosis should ensure appropriate therapy. When curative measures are no longer an option, it may be best to sedate the dying person so that they do not suffer this particular mental torment.

Acidosis can also be caused by other systems failing in their normal functioning. For example, the kidney may fail to excrete hydrogen ions, as can happen in renal diseases. Severe diarrhoea leads to excessive loss of bicarbonate ions (these are an important constituent of digestive secretions; Book 3, Chapter 3) and this too can cause death from acidosis (the equation on p. 76 is pulled to the right).

❑   Diabetes mellitus also causes acidosis. How can you explain this?

▨   In diabetes mellitus the cellular uptake of glucose may be insufficient for energy requirements to be met. The alternative energy substrates are fats, but when they are broken down they release fatty acids and hence the acidity of the extracellular fluid rises.

This account of the involvement of different bodily functions and their influence on the pH of body fluids is by no means exhaustive but it serves to indicate the web of interdependence. It follows that in the ageing body, when there is a generalized loss of function and systems have less reserve capacity to fall back on, it may take very little to push the body over the rather thin line between competence and failure. To name a specific cause of death may therefore be begging the question.

Summary of Section 3.6

1   Records show that most elderly people die of cardiovascular complications and yet the circulatory and associated respiratory system have tremendous reserve capacity.

2   Unfortunately, in Western societies the cardiovascular system tends to be unhealthy. Typically atherosclerosis develops from middle age onwards. This condition is exacerbated in those who also suffer from hypertension, diabetes or obesity.

3   Death occurs when tissues no longer receive adequate nutrients and waste products accumulate. This accumulation results in increased cellular acidity, known as acidosis. Acidosis is also caused by kidney failure, diabetes and severe diarrhoea.

4   Because of the interdependence of organ systems it may be pointless to name a specific cause of death in very old people.

3.7 Death

When does death actually occur? This might seem an easy question to answer, but it isn't.

The legal definition of death is one which is highly debated in national and religious courts. The term *clinical death* is used to describe those few minutes when the heart has stopped beating and breathing has ceased, but it is still theoretically possible to revive the patient. If clinical death occurs suddenly – for example in the cases of haemorrhage or a cardiac arrest – there is a short period before the cells lose their viability during which time first-aid measures such as heart massage and mouth-to-mouth resuscitation may be successful. Although most attempts to resuscitate someone fail, there are those that succeed; hence the continuation of the practice.

At the time of clinical death there may be a momentary period called the *agonal* phase. The term derived from the Greek *agon* meaning 'struggle'. When we speak of death agonies, we usually refer to muscle spasms induced by the blood's terminal acidity. This may be disturbing for those around, but the dying person is not likely to be aware of the spasms.

❑   Explain why this is so.

■   The brain is the first organ to fail when blood circulation ceases. This is because the brain can only use glucose for metabolism and it has no stores of glucose so is totally dependent on the supply brought by the blood circulatory system. Thus the dying person will no longer be conscious.

When death has occurred the face begins to change colour, and so a corpse looks quite different from someone who is unconscious. When attempting resuscitation those with medical experience know from the eyes whether this will be possible. Initially the eyes have a glassy look but within a few minutes they become dulled with the pupils dilating. After death the eyeballs begin to flatten out. Within a few hours, the body begins to shrink, obviously having lost air (hence the euphemism 'expired'). The lack of pulse indicates the cessation of circulation and the skin begins to look dull.

❑   Why does the skin change colour?

■   Oxygenated blood flowing just beneath the skin gives a 'bloom to living flesh. The change is seen most obviously in peoples of pale complexion, where the rosy glow of life gives way to a waxy pallor of death.

Once circulation ceases, all the cells of the body gradually stop functioning. Some cells live longer than others. You know that brain cells die very quickly but other cells last longer and can be used in transplant surgery. Without any artificial help kidney cells remain alive for half an hour after circulation ceases and, paradoxically, even heart cells stay alive for about 15 minutes. A few anaerobic processes (those requiring no oxygen) will continue for hours. One such is the liver cell's ability to break down alcohol.

The kind of fact much loved by writers of whodunnits, the supposedly well-known fact that hair and nails will keep growing for varying periods of time after death, is not a fact at all – no such thing happens.

❑   Explain why observers might think that hair and nails continue to grow.

■   The shrinking of the body's tissues will mean that a greater length of hair is exposed above the epidermis. Similarly, as the skin shrinks, the nails look longer.

Spasms of muscular activity are responsible for another gruesome-sounding aspect of death, the death rattle. Many inanimate objects can create sound, but sounds coming from a newly dead corpse are definitely scary. It is the tightening of laryngeal muscles at the same time as the air in the lungs is being expired that creates the sound of the death rattle.

Although newly dead muscle is flaccid, it becomes rigid within a few hours. This rigidity, known as *rigor mortis*, is a result of cross-linking of actin molecules in the muscles. As metabolism has ceased, the bonds are not broken.

❑   Which molecule is required to break the link?

◼   ATP (Book 3, Chapter 4).

Eventually, a few days later, the stiffness leaves the corpse as the lysosomal enzymes break down the actin cross-links, thereby slackening the muscles..

3.7.1 Defining death

Defining death is surprisingly difficult and has been attempted and questioned since time immemorial. In many societies, death was the moment when the soul left the body. As the soul couldn't be seen to leave, a more practical working definition was needed! One of the older monotheistic religions, Judaism, traditionally defined death as cessation of breathing for at least half an hour. Only after this could death be pronounced. However, with medical advances and knowledge about many death-like states, the definition of death has become the cause of great controversy.

The importance of having confidence in the certainty that death has occurred relates mostly to deaths following accidents – although the occasional tabloid tale of someone being found alive in a mortuary does nothing to dispel fears of being buried or burnt alive! The ability to use organs in transplants makes it vital that there are clear and uncontested criteria for death. Advances in medical technology make it possible to keep alive a person who ultimately has no hope for recovery. At times, issues around the right to die preoccupy society as a whole (through the involvement of the media) and not just medical ethicists and medical practitioners. It is useful to look at the recent history of the definition of death in order to understand why in the last 30 years *brainstem death* has become the benchmark.

Only since the 1960s have medical technologies been able to take over the functions of lungs and the heart. However, brain death was first raised in the literature at the start of the 20th century when there were reports of patients who had stopped breathing but whose hearts had continued to beat with the aid of artificial respiration for some hours afterwards.

Until this point, and indeed in many societies thereafter, the cessation of the heart was synonymous with death. Now it is generally accepted that, once the brainstem stops functioning, allowing essential processes to cease, recovery is impossible. The diagnosis of brainstem death has become the basis upon which life support machines for comatose patients are withdrawn.

The concept of total brain death as a category emerged in France in 1959 where it was described as death of the central nervous system and was characterized by persistent apnoeic (no breathing) coma, absent brainstem and tendon reflexes, and an electrically silent brain. It was not possible to detect any electrophysiological activity in either the superficial or deeper parts of these patients' brains. A decade later, in 1968, the Ad Hoc Committee of the Harvard Medical School to Examine the Definition of Brain Death published its four criteria to worldwide acclaim. These included:

1   the absence of cerebral responsiveness;

2   the absence of induced or spontaneous movement;

3   the absence of spontaneous respiration;

4   the absence of brainstem and deep tendon reflexes.

The use of an EEG (electroencephalogram) was not seen as mandatory but of confirmatory value. The report noted that hypothermia and drug intoxication might resemble brain death and recommended that for comatose patients tests be repeated over 24 hours to ensure the persistence of the condition.

As irreversible loss of brainstem function results in the dual inability to be conscious and breathe, Parris in the *Encyclopaedia Brittanica* (1987) notes that there are similarities between the medical definition and the traditional philosophical and religious based definitions such as the soul separating from the body.

While brainstem death remains in the UK the major criterion upon which death is decided, other formulations of brain death have gained credence. The higher brain formulation, for example, is sometimes used when referring to people in persistent vegetative states (PVS; those who breathe and appear conscious but do not react to any stimulus). One is then in the situation where one is arguing that one brain function is superior to another.

Problems arise when a patient deemed to be in a PVS is discovered to be in a 'locked-in syndrome'. Someone in a 'locked-in syndrome' will appear conscious and alert but unable to move any body part, speak or swallow and only communicate through blinking or voluntary eye movements. Recovery from this, unlike complete or partial recovery from a coma, is virtually unknown, but these people are conscious and aware of their surroundings. The vegetative state on the other hand is a medical diagnosis where the cerebral cortex has died but there is some brainstem function which enables the person to breathe unaided and heartbeat is spontaneous. If fed through a tube a person in this vegetative state can live for years.

A persistent vegetative state is one which is measured at more than one point in time over a long period. The Select Committee on Medical Ethics (1995) cited the definition of a 'vegetative state' provided by the American Medical Association Council on Scientific Affairs: 'a condition in which the body cyclically awakens and sleeps but expresses no behavioural or cerebral metabolic evidence of possession of cognitive function or being able to respond in a learned manner to external events and stimuli' (Walton, 1995).

Although patients with the 'locked-in syndrome' do not appear to outsiders to differ much from those with PVS, they are treated rather differently by their caregivers (Haig, 1994) and may live rather longer than those with PVS whose caregivers might not give them the same quality of care.

This debate entered the public arena in the UK in relation to a court case in 1992 where the parents of Tony Bland, a 21-year-old man in a persistent vegetative state, requested that artificial feeding be terminated. Tony Bland's chest had been crushed and he had therefore been deprived of oxygen three years' previously at the Hillsborough stadium in Sheffield (Figure 3.9). The five Law Lords in the House of Lords unanimously upheld the rulings of both the Court of Appeal and the High Court that doctors could withdraw the feeding tube conveying antibiotics, nutrition and hydration to enable Tony Bland 'to die peacefully with the greatest dignity and the least distress' (*British Medical Journal* (1992), **305**(2), p. 1312). The reason for the extensive legal action was to ensure that neither Tony Bland's doctor nor his parents could be prosecuted for murder through withdrawing antibiotics or feeding. Tony Bland died ten days later. This case made medical history in the UK because it affirmed that medical treatment included not only artificial ventilation but also hydration and artificial feeding.

Figure 3.9 Remembering those affected by the tragedy at the Hillsborough stadium, Sheffield.

At the same time as Tony Bland's fate was debated, Dr Nigel Cox, a Wessex rheumatologist, was convicted of giving a fatal injection of potassium chloride to Lilian Boyes, an older woman suffering intractable pain from rheumatoid arthritis and pleading to be enabled to die. Having obtained the consent of Mrs Boyes' family he recorded his actions in her notes. Some time after Mrs Boyes' cremation a Roman Catholic nurse read these notes and reported him to the authorities. Initially Dr Cox was charged with murder but this was changed to attempted murder and he was given a 12-month suspended sentence. In addition he appeared before the Professional Conduct Committee of the General Medical Council who did not rescind his license to practise but 'sentenced' him to a year's training in pain control and palliative care before he could practise once again as a consultant. The GMC recognized that Dr Cox 'acted in good faith in what you thought to be the best interests of your dying patient, and that your purpose was to relieve her intolerable suffering by expediting her death' (*British Medical Journal* (1992), **305**(2), p. 1311).

These two cases illustrate some important issues relating to curtailing life. First, that those in permanent vegetative states should have the possibility of being allowed to die, but only with the consent of the highest courts of the land. Secondly, that anyone experiencing excruciating pain has the right to adequate palliation and, by implication, that physicians should be competent at providing proper palliation.

Summary of Section 3.7

1   When death occurs there are irreversible changes in cells and tissues which are reflected in the appearance of the corpse.

2   Defining death is a very complex and controversial issue.

3   In the UK there are clear diagnostic guidelines indicating when it is permissible to turn off respirators for those who appear to be brain dead.

4   There is a continuing debate about how to define those in a persistent vegetative state and the circumstances in which they should be allowed to die.

3.8 Caring for and disposing of the body

The way in which the body is dealt with depends on the site of the death and the preference of the family or regulations of the institution. People who die at home may not be laid out in the conventional way, but simply called for by the undertaker who cleans the body. In hospitals, nurses usually lay out the body before the relatives are called (unless they are present at the death). This entails cleaning the body and changing the night clothes to make the deceased look as presentable, and life–like, as possible.

Once the family have visited or declined to do so, and a death certificate is issued, the body will be taken down to the mortuary for collection by an undertaker.

In relation to those from various traditions and cultures, there are clear regulations pertaining to what is and is not permitted to happen to the body. This varies between religions. For example, although most Hindus and Sikhs will allow nurses to carry out a limited laying out and removal of tubes such as feeding tubes, 'drips' or urine collecting tubes, where possible Jews and Muslims prefer that the body is not touched until collected by their own funeral directors.

Judaism, Islam, Sikhism and Hinduism have specific regulations regarding the care of the body. They attribute great significance to the obligation to lay out the body after death and prescribe certain practices. Although methods of disposal of the body differ, the soul is nevertheless seen as sacrosanct, and somewhat hampered from proceeding with its freedom from the body unless the body is disposed of very quickly.

Health workers are discouraged from touching Jewish bodies and encouraged to call religious authorities to remove them to expedite rapid burial. Deceased Jews and Muslims are washed in a ritual way by same-sex members of the religion prior to burial. During this procedure respect for the modesty of the body is paramount. Because of taboos associated with members of the other sex touching the body, Hindus and Sikhs prefer a similar process. The body will be ritually washed by same-sex relatives either in the funeral parlour or at home, and taken home for viewing. Men and older women are shrouded in white, young women in red. Sikhs who wore the 5Ks will wear them in death. The 5Ks are symbols of faith; a bracelet on the right wrist, a symbolic sword in a sheath, short trousers, uncut hair (which must remain covered by a turban if the deceased is male) and a wooden comb holding the hair. Obviously, professional carers need to understand the significance of these items to ensure that they are not disturbed after death.

With regard to the disposal of the body there are many different views about what is right and proper. As you might by now expect, these relate to culture and religion as well as personal preferences.

Ask some people you know, preferably from diverse backgrounds, their views about cremation and burial.

In your research, you probably found that some of your respondents had very strong views about burial and cremation, while others held more moderate views. Responses are likely to indicate a range of ecological, psychological and religious concerns.

Until 1885, cremation was unheard of in Britain, and for the following 50 years, it was still very rare. Since 1945 the pattern has reversed and in the late 1980s, other than in those countries where the religious norm is to cremate (e.g. India), England and Wales had the highest percentage of deceased who were cremated (70.5%) following Japan (95.7%). However, the incidence of cremation was lower in Scotland (55.6%) and exceedingly rare in Eire (1.5%).

Overcrowding of cemeteries was one of the main tenets of the pro-cremation movement a hundred years ago in the UK and viewed as a major public health problem. But as Leaney (1989) suggests, the move towards cremation also incorporated an 'intense loathing for human remains'. She suggests that cremation was a way to avoid confronting physical decay and represented an attempt to change the symbolism around death.

Most deaths are marked by a funeral service, regardless of whether the deceased is buried or cremated. The nature and location of the service will depend on the affiliation of the deceased and/or the principal mourners. With the increased secularization of society, many people are searching for alternative but meaningful ways to mark their own death. This might include making their own coffin or leaving precise instructions about the format of their own funeral, bypassing the religious organizations which might be viewed to have had the monopoly till now. The British Humanist Society, which is not a religious organization, has published guidelines on how to tailor ceremonies to the wishes of the deceased or mourners. These might include poetry readings, music or any other art form. The Natural Death Association also provides information for people who want to create their own funerals.

Christianity is the dominant religion in the UK and many funerals take place within the umbrella of the many different branches of the Christian church. Christians in the UK bury or cremate their dead. The service will usually take place in a church or a chapel near the crematorium and may include a Mass or Holy Communion. The body is then taken to the crematorium or cemetery and further prayers may be recited. Many mourning rituals, for example the wearing of black, have almost disappeared, but in some localities, and especially in Ireland, the rituals are sustained. Wakes are seen to provide considerable social support for the survivors.

Other religions represented in the UK continue to practise, in many cases, their age-old customs regarding disposal. Traditional Judaism forbids cremation and only permits burial in specially designated cemeteries. Bodies are buried in simple pine coffins following a ceremony in a chapel adjacent to the cemetery. Because in biblical times there was a recognition of the danger of diseases spread by putrefying bodies, Jews are buried as quickly as possible – preferably within two days of death. In recent times some non-affiliated Reform and Liberal Jews reject the categorical religious prohibition on cremation, and choose to be cremated. This usually take places in a municipal crematorium, sometimes under the auspices of a non–orthodox religious official.

Islam also prohibits cremation, and specifies burial in shrouds with the face of the deceased turned towards Mecca. However, as most British local authorities object to this custom, UK Muslims are usually buried in cemeteries in coffins. Hindus and Sikhs cremate their dead and, like Judaism and Islam, prefer rapid disposal. In India, Hindus view the body on the open pyre, but this is not permitted in the UK so viewing takes place at home before the coffin is closed. Services for Hindus and Sikhs have been devised for use at the crematorium, and the eldest son will signal the start of the cremation.

❏   What is the significance of a male giving this signal?

▄   Hindus believe that only a man's prayers can send a soul to heaven
        (Book 1, Chapter 4).

Hindu children under the age of 4 are viewed as too pure to be cremated and are buried; Sikhs sometimes follow this custom too. All initiated Sikhs are cremated, except babies who are buried. You will have noted that in each of these non-Christian religions cremation should take place as soon as possible; hence hospitals will try to ensure that delays with releasing the body are minimized.

Summary of Section 3.8

1   Different cultures define what is and is not permissible to do to a corpse prior to burial or other kind of disposal.

2   Depending on the religious tradition of the deceased and/or the preference of the deceased's family, certain procedures are carried out both immediately after death and prior to the funeral.

3   Although cremation is now the preferred form of disposal in the UK, certain religious traditions forbid this and legislate that burial should take place.

3.9 Bereavement, grief and mourning

Whether buried or cremated, the death of another human being has consequences for the living. The death of another may, depending on the circumstances and the relationship to the dead person, have a profound effect on those left behind. Losing a loved one is painful and can pose a serious threat to health and well-being.

Bereavement has over the past quarter of a century been subjected to a good deal of scrutiny. There exists a wealth of research that indicates that grief, the emotional reaction to bereavement, can render the individual vulnerable to a range of physical and mental symptoms. The classic studies of Colin Murray Parkes at Harvard University provide a range of evidence which links bereavement to mental and physical illness. Table 3.3 shows an increase in a range of psychic and somatic conditions in a sample of bereaved men and women in the Harvard research study (Parkes and Weiss, 1983).

Table 3.3   Harvard study of 68 bereaved men and women under 45 years of age compared, 14 months after bereavement, with the same number of non-bereaved subjects of the same age.

Feature	Number reporting feature		
	Bereaved	Non-bereaved	*P**
Admitted to hospital in past year	12	4	< 0.05
Trouble falling asleep in past year	19	8	< 0.02
Awakening during night in past year	27	8	< 0.001
Changes in appetite in past year	34	20	< 0.05
Big ups and downs in weight in past year	18	7	< 0.05
Increased alcohol consumption in past year	19	6	< 0.01
Taking tranquillizers in past year	18	3	< 0.001
Sought help for emotional problems in past year	23	5	< 0.001
Wonder if anything is worthwhile	34	18	< 0.01
Not too happy (multi-choice question)	13	4	< 0.05
Worried by loneliness (multi-choice)	44	17	< 0.001
Wish to change many parts of life (multi-choice)	15	5	< 0.05
Depressed or very unhappy in past few weeks	33	20	< 0.05
Experienced restlessness in past year	33	15	< 0.01
Memory not all right in past year	20	6	< 0.01
Hard to make up mind in past year	36	22	< 0.05
Life often a strain	25	12	< 0.05
Judgement not too good	28	14	< 0.02
Feel somewhat apart or remote even among friends	23	10	< 0.01
It's safer not to fall in love	13	2	< 0.02

* Probability values:
P < 0.05 represents a small significant difference;
P < 0.01 represents a strong significant difference;
P < 0.001 represents a very strong significant difference.

For all the features listed in Table 3.3, the bereaved show a significant increase in symptoms compared to the non-bereaved. An increased tendency to drink more alcohol, take more tranquillizers and to have sleep problems are all apparent. Mainly they are symptoms of mental malaise but Parkes has also found links – particularly in bereaved married men – to increased mortality from cardiovascular disease. However, he is careful to point out that these are not causal but correlational links. Figure 3.10 shows how the mortality of widowers in the first six months after the death of their spouse was 40% higher than the expected rate of deaths for married men of similar ages.

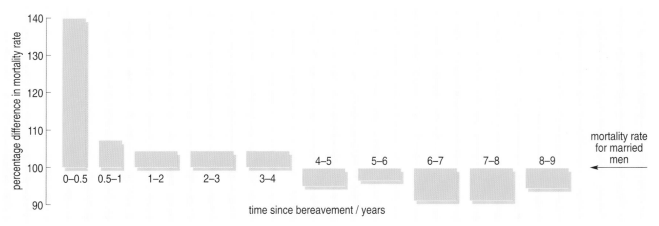

Figure 3.10 Mortality rate of widowers aged over 54 as a percentage of the rate for married men of the same age.

3.9.1 Reactions to death

It is now well documented that a common and some would say universal reaction to the death of a loved one is shock. This emotion can be described as an environmental stressor to distinguish it from the physiological condition of shock. Even if the death was expected, the actual event and the experience of loss is acutely felt. It is therefore not difficult to imagine from what we know of the body's reaction to environmental stressors (Book 4, Chapter 5) – raised blood pressure and pulse rate, palpitations, sweating and acute anxiety – that this could have an adverse affect on the cardiovascular system.

After the initial shock, the full realization of the loss can be extremely painful and the word 'pining' has been used to describe the emotional experience. But in fact people describe a whole range of feelings which include anger, depression, anxiety, acute loneliness even if surrounded by family and friends, and a sense of desolation. It is no wonder that people find it hard to sleep, relax, concentrate and generally function mentally when they are experiencing such turmoil.

Some bereavements are thought to be so traumatic that a specific syndrome has been identified and named and recorded in the *Diagnostic and Statistical Manual of the American Psychiatric Association* (Lucas and Seiden, 1987). This is known as 'post-traumatic stress syndrome'. It is experienced by people who are involved in mass disasters or horrific accidents (such as occurred at Hillsborough; Figure 3.9), or when they experience the death of a loved one through murder or suicide. The symptoms in Box 3.3 describe the syndrome.

Box 3.3   Symptoms of post-traumatic stress syndrome

People suffering from this disorder:

Re-experience the trauma in one of the following ways:

- They have recurrent recollections of the event.

- They have dreams of the events.

- They suddenly feel as if the event were recurring.

Experience a numbing or reduced involvement with the world by:

- A lessening of interest in important activities.

- A feeling of detachment from others.

- A flat, emotionless feeling.

Have some of the following symptoms:

- Sleep disturbances

- Guilt about surviving.

- Trouble concentrating, loss of memory.

- Exaggerated startle response.

- They avoid some of the activities that arouse recollections of the trauma.

3.9.2 Grieving

Clearly some deaths cause more mental distress than others. The Society of Compassionate Friends – a self-help agency for all those who have experienced the loss of a child – maintain that there is no death so sad as the death of a child for a parent. On the other hand, the death of a spouse can involve many other losses such as loss of income, loss of a sexual partner, loss of identity as well as the loss of a valued person. Whatever the circumstances, the loss may represent relief if the person was suffering. In a different context, where a relationship has been oppressive, death brings liberation. Even so, the feelings generated can be difficult to deal with especially as people often feel guilty in such situations. It is invidious and unfruitful to differentiate between each individual's experience of grief.

Grief hurts, and the process of grieving is an attempt to heal the emotional wound. Just as the body has mechanisms for healing physical wounds (as you saw in Book 1) so the mind has the capacity to heal its wounds. Just how it does this remains largely a mystery in many ways, because individuals vary so much in how they react to their grief. But there are many theories about what helps and what hinders the healing process.

Mourning rituals can be interpreted as an attempt to heal the breach left in a community by the death of one of its members, and in a more individualistic framework the same mourning rituals can help to heal the individual's wounds. Examples of these are the Irish wake, which takes place in the period after the death and funeral, and the Jewish year of mourning, where other Jews rally round to support the mourners emotionally and practically and reintegrate them back into society after the first week (*shiva*) following the funeral. Rituals therefore provide a structure and timetable for grief and usually prescribe support from other members of the community. Those following religious traditions which delineate specific mourning practices find these comforting and reassuring.

In the absence of a religious or cultural code, a process of grieving has been adopted in Western societies which also sets out a pattern of grieving and a framework for behaviour and has almost taken on a ritualistic significance. It is a pattern of grieving which is used a great deal by bereavement counsellors. It is thought that the bereaved must work through certain stages if they are to heal their emotional wounds. Worden (1982) described the tasks of mourning as shown in Box 3.4.

Box 3.4   Worden's four tasks of mourning

Task 1 is to accept the reality of the loss, to come to terms with the shock and disbelief that is very common immediately after a bereavement.

Task 2 is to experience the pain of grief. Giving vent to anger and acknowledging the pain is considered to be cathartic.

Task 3 is to adjust to an environment from which the deceased is missing. Worden believes that feelings of anxiety and helplessness and lost of self-confidence have to be dealt with if the bereaved person is to overcome their grief.

Task 4 is to withdraw emotional energy from the lost person and reinvest it in another relationship or activity.

Many people feel uncomfortable with such a prescriptive formula, especially when it is accompanied by expected timescales. Yet how often do we make assumptions about how long it is reasonable for someone to grieve? 'You'd think she'd be over it by now' is a common sentiment when someone goes on shedding tears one, two or more years after the death of a loved one. Bereaved people are acutely aware of the expectations of others and often hide their feelings so as not to offend some expected code of behaviour. Many bereaved people object to their private grief being squeezed into a particular mould which they feel does not fit. And many say that their wounds do not heal, that they go on feeling hurt and sad but they also go on living their lives. For, unlike the case of a physical wound, some people manage to live with their emotional wound without it festering or infecting the rest of their system. Whatever healing means, it rarely involves forgetting. It is the ability to remember a lost loved one with warmth and affection which is perhaps the most desired outcome of grief.

3.9.3 Remembering the dead

We remember the dead in both formal and informal ways. This remembering is of great significance to those left behind. Epitaphs, obituaries, monuments and memorials are public forms of remembering (Figure 3.11). More private ways of remembering are photos, letters, articles of clothing or other cherished mementoes. Revisiting favourite places or listening to shared tunes all can vividly bring back the memory of a dead person. The act of writing about a dead person is very therapeutic for some people.

Figure 3.11   Anglo-Saxon cross in churchyard, Eyam, Derbyshire.

One bereaved mother explained:

> I would feel that I just had to write about Amanda. Because she was so lovely, I was afraid of forgetting her, or other people forgetting her and I wanted to write down some of the things that she did but she did so many things that it was so hard, so I just focused on little points and little memories, that I liked that appealed to me. And once I had written them down, I felt they were safe and that I would never forget them and I could show them perhaps to brothers and sisters when they grew up or I could just keep them private or just, you know, they were mine, they were special, they were precious, and they became very sacred to me, you know. I felt as though I had still got a piece of her if I had written it down. So in two ways it helped because it created memories that I could read and reread and it also helped to express the anger and the pain and the hurt, getting that out and sort of unloading it so that then I was free to think of what I was going to do for the rest of my life. So we started to publish this newsletter and we found that a lot of other parents too found comfort in writing, a kind of therapy and other parents, who didn't find that they could write, enjoyed reading it and could say, well yes, I felt like that, I know how that person feels. And sometimes somebody would look at a poem and say, yes, I know that person.

Many people now create their own memories for their loved ones before they die. Some even make videos for their family and friends to view after their death. Dying people leave remnants of themselves behind in many different ways. Some do so through creative work such as paintings or poetry; others write letters or leave personal belongings. This urge to leave a personal legacy has been recognized as therapeutic and some hospices have writers or artists in residence to work with dying people to help them create their lasting memorials.

In the final chapter of this book we examine legacies in more detail. We look at the legacies left by individuals as well as the legacy that our current society may be leaving for future generations.

Summary of Section 3.9

1 Following the death of a loved one, bereaved people are more likely to develop physical or mental ill-health.

2 Mental and physical ill-health can also follow the experience of observing a severe trauma, such as a mass disaster. This is termed post-traumatic stress syndrome.

3 Mourning rituals vary between different cultural groups and are seen to provide a structure for grieving.

4 Mourning has been divided into four tasks (Worden) but there are critiques of prescriptive timetables such as these.

5 Memorials can be created in a variety of ways and are believed to be healing in themselves.

Objectives for Chapter 3

After completing this chapter you should be able to:

3.1 Define and use, or recognize definitions and applications of, each of the terms printed in **bold** in the text.

3.2 Appreciate that attitudes to death and dying have changed over time and that they also depend on religious and cultural affiliations. (*Question 3.1*)

3.3 Understand and explain some of the problems encountered in the treatment of pain. (*Question 3.2*)

3.4 Explain why cardiovascular disease is so often cited on death certificates. (*Question 3.3*)

3.5 Explain why failures in a variety of different organ systems can each result in acidosis. (*Question 3.3*)

3.6 Describe the different definitions of death that have been used over the ages. (*Question 3.4*)

3.7 Explain why defining death is important. (*Question 3.4*)

3.8 Appreciate that different cultures and religions have different rituals associated with dying, caring for and disposing of the body. (*Question 3.5*)

3.9 Illustrate some of the health consequences of bereavement and the strategies used to adjust successfully to this new status. (*Question 3.6*)

Questions for Chapter 3

Question 3.1 (*Objective 3.2*)

What factors have contributed to the removal of death from the home to the hospital in the 20th century?

Question 3.2 (*Objective 3.3*)

In what ways has the rise of the hospice movement contributed to the improved care for dying people?

Question 3.3 (*Objectives 3.4 and 3.5*)

Explain how a sluggish circulation can lead to acidosis.

Question 3.4 (*Objectives 3.6 and 3.7*)

In what way was the case of Tony Bland an important precedent in British law?

Question 3.5 (*Objective 3.8*)

How might the place where a person died affect the subsequent treatment of the body?

Question 3.6 (*Objective 3.9*)

When are Worden's four tasks of mourning unhelpful?

References

Ariès, P. (1974) *Western Attitudes towards Death*, Johns Hopkins University Press, Baltimore and London.

Glaser, B. and Strauss, B. (1965) *Awareness of Dying*, Aldine, Chicago.

Glaser, B. and Strauss, B. (1968) *Time for Dying*, Aldine, Chicago.

Jennett, B. (1992) Letting vegetative patients die, *British Medical Journal*, **305(2)**, pp. 1305–6; and also two news items in same issue: High Court rules doctors can stop feeding Tony Bland, p. 1312; GMC tempers justice with mercy in Cox case, p. 1311.

Mulkay, M. and Ernst, J. (1991) The changing profile of social death, *Archives Européenes de Socio*logie **32**, pp. 172–96.

O'Brien, M. D. (1990) Criteria for diagnosing brainstem death, *British Medical Journal*, **301**, pp. 108–9.

Parkes, C. M. (1972) *Bereavement: Studies of Grief in Adult Life*, International Universities Press, New York.

Regnard, C. and Davies, A. (1986) *A Guide to Symptom Relief in Advanced Cancer*, Haigh and Hochland Ltd, Manchester.

Sudnow, D. (1967) *Passing On: the Social Organisation of Dying*, Prentice Hall, Englewood Cliffs, New York.

Select Committee on Medical Ethics (chair: Walton, Lord of Detchant) (1995) Dilemmas of life and death: part one, *Journal of the Royal Society of Medicine*, **88**, pp. 311–15.

Walter, T. (1994) *The Revival of Death*, Routledge, London.

CHAPTER 4
A HEALTHY PLANET

4.1 Introduction

As promised at the very beginning of this course we will now try to place human biology in a wider setting, remembering the importance of our environment, in the broadest of senses. To be able to understand the importance of the environment for our health, we need to know a little about the interdependence between environment and humankind. This chapter will look at interactions between plants, animals and the physical and chemical environment, as well as considering ways in which humans have altered, and are altering this environment. These changes have health implications that are not always immediately obvious. Frequently, we initiate changes that are going to have their effects some time in the future, and we will be looking at the legacies that we leave to future generations. This chapter will begin, however, at the more personal level. In the previous chapter we concluded with the emotional and physical health of those who have been bereaved, and now we move on to consider our own demise, and ask what exactly it is we think we will be leaving for those who follow.

4.2 Legacies and inheritance

There is no doubt that each one of us affects the lives of those who surround us. Many of our interactions with others are very obvious to us and could be described in terms of personal, professional and social relationships. But there are other, often unnoticed, interactions: the mother taking her children to school, the man buying his paper, the youth at the bus stop – all people we see regularly and only notice when they are not there. Younger people are often very worried about what others think of them behind their back, 'when they are not there'. Older people tend to replace this worry with a concern about how they will be viewed after their death, 'when they are not there'.

How would you like to be remembered? Write your own epitaph. (How widely do you hope to be remembered? How do you visualize this coming about?)

There will be a few whose lifetime achievements will be immortalized in print, on newsreels and on celluloid but most of us can neither expect nor hope to be remembered in such a way. Rather, we look in particular at our closest friends and family and speculate on how they would carry on without us. If we have descendants, we may have made provision for them. This seems such a natural thing to do that we scarcely give a thought as to why we care for them preferentially.

❑   What is the biological basis for this behaviour?

◼   Our children inherit genes from us, so we could be said to be providing a favourable environment for the continued existence of these ('our') genes.

Interestingly, the old adage that 'maternity is a matter of fact whereas paternity is a matter of opinion', is reflected in the inheritance laws of some cultures where property and other possessions pass through the maternal line.

❑   Can you think of other ways in which behavioural differences between men and women might reflect certainty, or uncertainty, of paternity?

◼   1   In many societies and cultures, women's behaviour is carefully monitored and controlled by the family to ensure that no inappropriate sexual activity takes place. Examples are the placing of women in purdah, not allowing them out of the house without a chaperone.

2   The greater the number of successful matings that an individual achieves, the higher the proportion of their genes left in the population in future generations. Women can only give birth at approximately 9-month intervals, whereas (theoretically) men can father large numbers of children in that time. Consequently, a tendency to promiscuous behaviour is more likely to be found in men than in women.

3   In most societies, women devote more of their energy (i.e. their somatic effort) to their children's upbringing, than do men.

You may have thought of other examples. Our behaviour is not driven solely by our biology. There are many people who are parents for children to whom they are not biologically related. Also, many people arrange for part or all of their material assets to pass to organizations or individuals to whom they are not related. These organizations are often those with a role in health care, such as Sight Savers, MacMillan Nurses and the Marie Curie Foundation, amongst many others.

However, as we end this course we are more concerned with wider issues of inheritance and these have to do with the ways in which humankind, as a species, is altering its own environment. What effects does this have on individuals, and on populations? Are we leaving a healthy planet for our descendants?

Summary of Section 4.2

We are biologically predisposed to provide for our offspring and may try to ensure that this provision continues after our death. However, our interactions with other members of society are wide-ranging and many people leave legacies to benefit the wider community.

4.3 Altering the environment

In subsequent sections of this chapter, we will be considering a number of ways in which humans alter their environment.

❏   In what ways do you think we are altering the environment ?

■   There are numerous possible answers here and our list is not exhaustive. Most people would point to the built environment, the creation of towns and cities and their industrial base, before moving on to the pollution that goes with a modern lifestyle. If you thought about the clearing of tropical rainforests, you might have appreciated that the temperate forests have also largely gone to make way for agricultural land. You might have global warming and the extinction of species down on your list too.

We will be looking at all these ideas, but it is worth pointing out that we are about to consider a number of topics that are very complex and fraught with uncertainties. Even if we devoted more time to them we would still be unable to fully answer the question of what we should do to ensure a healthy planet. It is clear that humans are not unique in affecting their environment. Many large mammals make very noticeable changes to their environment. For example, the passage of a herd of elephants through an area can be as obvious as the visit of a plague of locusts. Not only does their feeding behaviour destroy woodland, but other species are destroyed as they trample around their feeding area. Like hippopotamuses, they enjoy a watery wallow and thereby transform clear pools into areas of 'mud, mud, glorious mud' (to quote a well-known song!).

All species alter their environment to some extent, and you may be able to think of examples of this, particularly if you own pets.

Spend a minute or two listing such examples.

Cat owners often notice that there are fewer birds nesting in their gardens than in neighbouring ones, which is just one example of the more general observation that carnivores reduce the numbers of their prey species. The effects of herbivores grazing will be familiar to any gardener with a slug or rabbit problem, as will the beneficial effects of earthworms aerating the soil. Brown patches of dead grasses often appear after the ground has been urinated upon by dogs or horses, demonstrating clearly that too much nitrogen has a detrimental effect on vegetation in the short-term. All of these interactions remind us that many organisms share physical space and coexist in a state of dynamic equilibrium. The study of these interactions is the subject matter of the branch of biology known as **ecology**, but unravelling the details of the extent of the interdependence of organisms is unnecessarily complex for our purposes. However, we will spend a little time gaining some background information so that we can put our own activities into context.

Summary of Section 4.3

All species alter their environment to some extent because they do not live in isolation from one another. The study of the interactions between plants, animals and their environment is known as ecology.

4.4 Ecology: some background information

The environment in which any organism lives is known as its **habitat**. It will share its habitat with other organisms, who are themselves part of the habitat. A habitat has distinctive physical and chemical features.

❑   Can you give any examples, from general knowledge, of the physical and chemical features of your habitat?

◼   Obviously this depends on where you live, but you might have noted conditions of temperature and rainfall. You will be aware of hilly, undulating or flat surroundings. The quality of the underlying terrain may be less obvious, but if you have travelled around a little you may have noticed trees and shrubs that are common in some areas are rare in others. If you are a gardener, you might have attributed this to factors such as the soil quality, being familiar with the concept that plants have quite narrow tolerances. For example, some plants such as camellias are unable to thrive on a chalky, lime-rich soil (such a soil is described as mildly alkaline and has a high pH value) whereas others, like wild thyme, cannot grow in a peaty soil (very acidic with a low pH value).

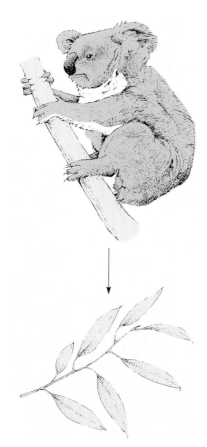

Figure 4.1 An example of a food chain involving *Eucalyptus* and the koala. Note that koala are totally dependent on *Eucalyptus*. They do not eat any other plant.

Habitats can be quite varied, even over relatively small distances. A pond, wood and meadow all provide different habitats, but even so, some organisms may move between habitats (perhaps at different times of the year). For example, a bird might feed on seeds from early-flowering woodland plants and later progress to grass seeds from the meadow. When organisms have very precise habitat requirements, the loss of that aspect of the environment has serious consequences. It is well known that koala must have a diet of leaves from certain species of *Eucalyptus*, and given the importance of the koala to the Australian tourist industry we might expect that every care will be taken to ensure that their dietary needs are met. The relationship between these two organisms can be expressed as a *food chain* (see Figure 4.1). In a food chain plants are described as *primary producers*. Plants are eaten by herbivores, termed *primary consumers*; in their turn these animals may be eaten by carnivores, who will be *secondary consumers*.

Although it is slow-moving, an adult koala weighs around 10 kg and has strong claws so lacks natural predators. However, koalas were driven close to extinction in the early part of the 20th century because people killed them for their skin (rather than their flesh). They will just as surely become extinct if we destroy their food source. Nor is this a remote possibility. But Australians are now more aware of the ecological implications of clearing the bush, for urban development for example.

The *Eucalyptus* provides food for other species too, so a more realistic way of expressing the complicated interrelationships of plants and animals, is in a *food web* as shown in Figure 4.2 for the common oak.

❑   This figure does not tell the whole story; in what way is it incomplete?

▨   The figure does not show what happens to the organisms in the food web when they die.

There are many organisms that feed on dead organic matter: animals such as earthworms, called *detritivores*, and soil fungi and bacteria, termed *decomposers*. Note that most animals are able to use more than one species for food and are, in turn, preyed upon by a variety of other animals. This reduces the vulnerability of a species but it also makes it very difficult for ecologists to predict the outcome of an alteration in the availability of any one food source for the other populations in the food web.

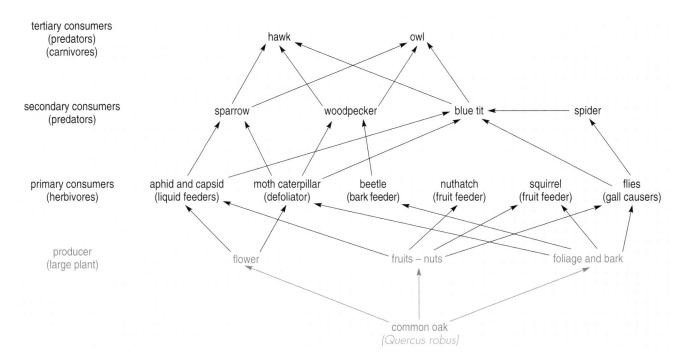

Figure 4.2   A generalized food web.

All the nutrients in a food web derive from the producers (also referred to as 'primary producers'. These use solar energy and simple chemicals to build organic molecules. The process is called **photosynthesis**. The net amount of organic compound accumulating in plants is called *net primary production (NPP)*. It is measured as the productivity of an area over a specified time. (You might come across the term gross primary production. This is a measure of the total energy captured by the plants. It exceeds the NPP by a value equal to the amount of energy lost in plant respiration.) A glance at Table 4.1 shows the tremendous variability in productivity between different **ecosystems** (an ecosystem is a unit comprising several habitats and the organisms within them). This is of enormous economic importance to us. NPP is available to herbivores and, via herbivores, to carnivores as food. However, humans are unique in making further and different uses of plant material.

Table 4.1   Average values for net primary production (NPP) in different ecosystems.

Ecosystem	NPP/kJ per square metre per year
extreme desert	260
desert scrub	2 600
subsistence agriculture	3 000
open ocean	4 700
areas over continental shelf	13 500
temperate grasslands	15 000
temperate deciduous forest	26 000
intensive agriculture	30 000
tropical forest	40 000

❏   For what purposes other than food do we use plants?

▦   Clothing (e.g. cotton and flax); housing and furniture (e.g. timber); energy (e.g. timber and peat); medicines (e.g. witch hazel, willow and yew); transport (e.g. rubber and hemp).

Unfortunately, not all of the NPP from the primary producers is available to carnivores. As well as using energy and materials for growth, the herbivores will have used energy in various other metabolic processes, principally respiration; there is also considerable loss as heat and also in faeces. To sustain a carnivorous diet requires a much greater input of NPP than is necessary for an herbivorous diet. In terms of numbers, there are far more plants than animals and more herbivores than carnivores. This is represented in Figure 4.3 as a pyramid of numbers. There are many more species and individuals at lower levels than there are at higher levels. Each organism occupies a particular feeding level or *trophic* level. On average, the transfer of energy from one trophic level to the next is only about 10% of the energy potentially available.

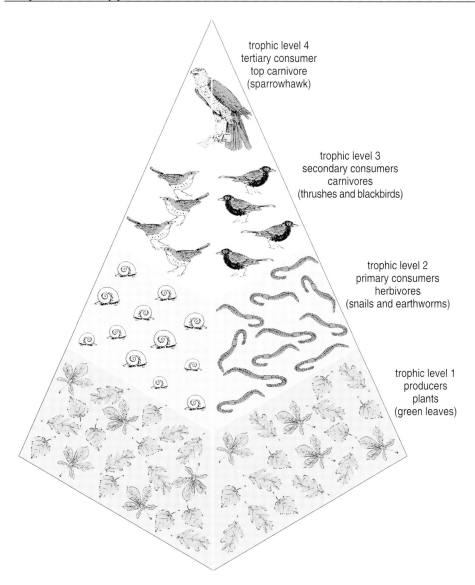

Figure 4.3   A pyramid of numbers. (Note that earthworms are both primary consumers *and* detritivores.)

Many organisms (ourselves included) can feed at more than one trophic level, and this is just one of the factors that makes unravelling the interactions within a habitat so complex. It is very easy to see how the fortunes of populations of one species can have a knock-on effect on other species, but it is not always possible to predict exactly which species will be most affected by any novel changes.

There are three factors that can check the growth of any animal population: disease, predation and limitations of the food supply. You might remember that in Book 1, Chapter 4, this was expressed for human populations as disease, war and famine.

Figure 4.4 shows the way in which the populations of the lynx and the snowshoe hare have fluctuated over 90 years. Notice that the peaks in one population are always followed by peaks in the other population.

❏   Why is this second peak always lower than the first peak?

■   This is an example of the pyramid of numbers. The prey species (snowshoe hare) is always more numerous than the predator (lynx).

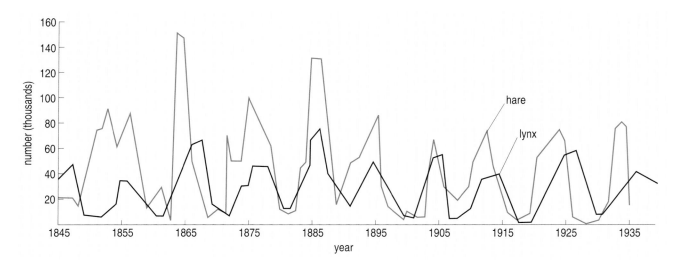

Figure 4.4   Changes in abundance of a predator–prey system: the lynx, *Lynx canadensis*, and the snowshoe hare, *Lepus americanus*.

Predator–prey relations are seldom as straightforward as this, because most predators do not rely on a single prey species. In the same way, the relationship between koala and *Eucalyptus* is unusual because most herbivores eat a varied diet. Any species with a specialized diet, or indeed any other specialized habitat requirement, is vulnerable to the specific loss of that resource. However, most ecological investigations reveal more complex interrelationships than these. Hence interference with the members of one species within an ecosystem can have unpredictable results, as we shall see in the next section.

Summary of Section 4.4

The relationships between plants and animals can be expressed as food chains and food webs. In both cases the primary producers are plants and they provide all the energy within the system (chain or web) by a process called photosynthesis. The systems can support fewer carnivores than herbivores because energy is lost from one trophic level to the next. This idea is shown diagrammatically as the pyramid of numbers. Because relationships within a food web are variable and complex we cannot accurately predict the effect of losing one species from the web.

4.5 Changes in relative abundance of species

There are a number of ways in which humans have altered ecosystems, that
have led to the decline of particular species. We will leave to one side any
major interference such as felling forests to provide land for agricultural
and urban development, and instead begin by examining examples where
we have eroded or eradicated stocks of particular species. This has notably
been a consequence of the over-exploitation of food species (prey items).
Predators do not normally eliminate their prey (see Figure 4.4), but the use
of sophisticated tools, such as guns and fishing gear, has led to our being
over-successful as hunters. The disappearance of the dodo must surely be
the best-known example, but it is not an isolated occurrence. Table 4.2
shows some other vertebrate extinctions that correlate with human activity.
This table gives a selection of species only. For example, around 100 species
of bird are known to have become extinct since 1600.

Table 4.2   Some vertebrate extinctions.

Species	Former distribution	Last recorded	Probable cause of extinction
Birds			
dodo	Mauritius	*c.* 1680	hunting
great auk	North Atlantic	1844	hunting by sailors
passenger pigeon	North America	1889	hunting and habitat destruction
pink-headed duck	Bengal	1936	hunting
Mammals			
auroch	Europe	1627	hunting and habitat destruction
Caribbean monk seal	Caribbean	*c.* 1960	hunting
Steller's sea cow	North Pacific	1768	hunting
Tasmanian wolf	Tasmania	1900s	hunted as a 'pest'
Fish			
harelip sucker	rivers of North America	1893	fishing and habitat destruction
blue pike	Great Lakes, North America	1970	over-fishing, pollution, predation by introduced fish species
Reptile			
St Croix racer	St Croix, US Virgin Isles	1900s	

We are also guilty of importing exotic species, some of which, like the
rhododendron (imported from Asia to Europe), have run riot in the absence
of natural predators or primary consumers, and so have tended to out-
compete native plants. Sometimes introductions have been accidental; rats
and many disease-causing organisms have spread around the world via
relatively modern transportation such as sailing ships. However, deliberate

introductions, such as the rhododendron, have been made with worthy intentions. On a number of occasions animals have been introduced to new habitats in an attempt to limit the populations of pest species. This is known as **biological control**. In the first half of the 20th century, the American giant toad, *Bufo marinus*, was introduced into a number of Caribbean islands and then into agricultural land on Hawaii, the Philippines, Fiji and some other Polynesian Islands. In all these areas, it was reported to limit successfully the numbers of a variety of insect pests. As a result, when sugar cane farmers in Northern Australia faced heavy losses because two indigenous species of beetle had taken a great fancy to this relatively newly introduced crop, it seemed sensible to see whether these toads could eradicate the beetles. The first toads were brought into Australia in 1935 and a breeding colony was established in Queensland. Tadpoles and toadlets were given to farmers in beer bottles and jam jars from which they were released into suitable areas of the sugar cane fields. The results were disastrous. The toads took to their new country and spread like wild-fire but they didn't eat the beetle pests. They ate many harmless insects and even beneficial ones, like honey-bees. Their tough skin secretes toxins, protecting the toad from predation and often poisoning the would-be predator. Within five years of their introduction, the toads, which became known as the 'cane toads', were designated as vermin. However, they have been surprisingly difficult to eradicate. Although mammalian and avian (bird) predators have learnt to avoid them, reptiles and amphibians seem to have become rare in the areas where these toads are common. This could be a result of direct encounters but it might also be because of indirect competition for food. So here we have an example of the unexpected outcome of an attempt to manipulate a food web. Scientists had predicted, wrongly, that the toads would occupy the same niche in this new community as they had when introduced to other, apparently similar, habitats.

Not all change is a direct result of human intervention. Sometimes changes can occur over which we have little control. One such example is the case of Dutch elm disease (so-called because most of the early studies of the disease were carried out in Holland, although the disease was first observed in France in 1918). The disease is caused by a fungus, *Ceratocystis ulmi*, that has the elm, *Ulmus procera*, as its only habitat and food source. Spores of the fungus are carried by the elm bark beetle, *Scolytus scolytus*, which feeds on the shoots and young bark of the elm. The beetles breed in the bark of elms, so there needs to be some damage already present to allow them to get under the bark. Once the spores get under the bark, the fungus can start to spread. As the fungus can grow alongside the developing beetle larvae, the newly emerged beetles will themselves carry spores and spread the disease as they fly to new trees. The fungus produces toxins and it also blocks vessels as it grows in the elm. The result of this is that the leaves wilt and the branches die back. Figure 4.5 shows the cycle of activity.

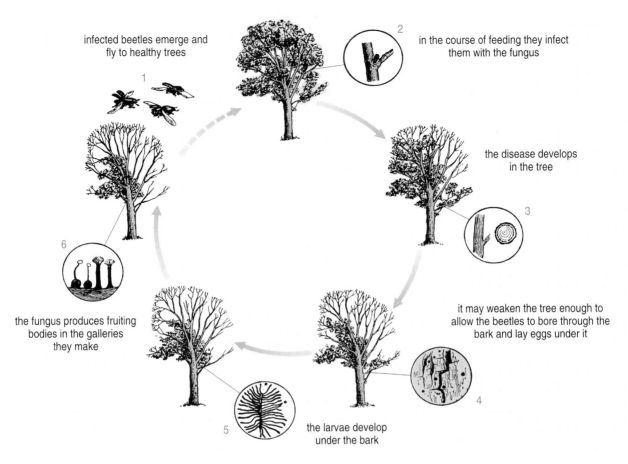

infected beetles emerge and
fly to healthy trees

1

2

in the course of feeding they infect
them with the fungus

the disease develops
in the tree

3

it may weaken the tree enough to
allow the beetles to bore through the
bark and lay eggs under it

4

6

the fungus produces fruiting
bodies in the galleries
they make

5

the larvae develop
under the bark

Elm trees mostly recover from these attacks and the wood, which is used in the furniture industry, can be utilized without loss of value should the tree die. So you would be right in thinking that no serious efforts were made to eradicate the disease. Indeed, by the 1930s it had spread to the USA, probably carried by imported veneer-quality timber. But the elm has considerable amenity value: it is attractive in hedgerows and avenues and is particularly useful as a town tree because it is resistant to fumes and pollutants. For this reason some town councils did take steps to curb the spread of the disease.

During the 1970s the fungus suddenly and inexplicably became more virulent, causing the death of the trees. The elm has been virtually wiped out in the UK. For example, in the whole of southern England the only places where you can still see mature elms are in Brighton and Hastings.

❏   Can you suggest why the elm remains in these two places?

■   Their councils were prepared to put sufficient resources into efficient eradication of any outbreaks. They were probably further helped by the natural barrier of the treeless South Downs, and the prevalence of onshore winds tending to blow the beetles back across the downs if they started to swarm seaward.

Figure 4.5   Diagram showing the life cycle of the fungus *Ceratocystis ulmi*, the cause of Dutch elm disease, and its connection with the elm bark beetles, *Scolytus scolytus*.

In the north of England and in Scotland, the closely related species, the wych elm, *Ulmus glabra,* is surviving. One difference between the two species is that, whilst the elm usually propagates by means of suckers (these are, in effect, asexual clones of the parent plant), the wych elm is normally reared from seed and therefore has a broader genetic base. In other words, there is more genetic variation in the population.

❑   Why is genetic variation important?

▓   The more variation there is between members of a species, the better the chance that, in a changing environment, there will be some individuals that have the ability to thrive (or at least survive!) in the new conditions (Book 1, Chapter 1).

It is for this reason that there are now international agreements on the need to work together to retain genetic diversity in all species and, more generally, biological diversity (species *and* habitat diversity).

❑   From a practical point of view, can you suggest some species where retaining genetic diversity is of particular importance to humankind?

▓   Any species that we exploit for food or other materials is of practical importance to us.

When we cultivate a plant or domesticate an animal, we tend to breed and select for desirable features: heavy yield, fast maturing or low fat to meat ratio, for example. Because only a few 'good' plants are selected to be parents of the next generation, this tends to reduce the genetic variability within the species. So work is currently in progress to try and ensure that we do not lose the potential for reintroducing variability. This is done through schemes such as the rare breeds societies and seed banks like the one in Nicaragua for tropical hardwood seeds, and the Kew Gardens Millenium Seed Appeal in the UK.

We have already said that the blame for loss of species from particular habitats cannot always be laid at our door. An example here is the loss of the elm through Dutch elm disease. Regrettably, there are well-documented cases such as the dodo where we, or our ancestors, are clearly to blame. Despite the fact that, as far as we can tell from the fossil record, extinctions are a normal part of evolution, the current *rate* of extinction is the cause of our concern. The fossil record shows five major extinction episodes have taken place over the past 500 million years, but the fear is that

> *... humanity has initiated the sixth great extinction spasm, rushing to eternity a large fraction of our fellow species in a single generation.*
> *(E. O. Wilson, 1992)*

You may feel that this is alarmist, given that the Earth recovered from the other five episodes, but consider the time-scales. Previous mass extinctions (the most recent of which put paid to the dinosaurs some 66 million years ago), are presumed to have taken place over several million years, with the recovery to similar levels of diversity taking up to 20 million years. At the present time, extinctions are occurring most rapidly in the tropics, yet, even in Britain it is estimated that around 6% of our species have become extinct during the 20th century.

❏   Why should we worry about this?

■   Once a species becomes extinct it has gone for ever. We depend on other species for our livelihoods and our health.

This is well explained in publicity material from the Royal Botanic Gardens, Kew (Figure 4.6 and Box 4.1).

Figure 4.6   Cover from the Kew Gardens Millennium Seed Bank Appeal leaflet.

Box 4.1   Extract from the leaflet for the Kew Gardens Millennium Seed Bank Appeal

We're collecting for the sake of every species.

Over the next 50 years, a quarter of the world's seed-bearing plant species will face extinction. It's a terrifying thought, especially when the future of every species will then be put at risk – including ours.

We simply can't survive without plants. We need them for the air we breathe, the food we eat, and the medicines we use to combat disease. Some give us natural insecticides, reducing the use of chemicals on crops; others have the ability to reclaim land lost to the desert.

In all, over 250 000 seed-bearing plants work together to make our world habitable and beautiful. With every species that disappears, part of the fabric of the planet crumbles; and priceless genetic information is lost forever.

Conservation saves lives.

An enormous seed collection programme has already begun. It's perhaps the most ambitious conservation project of its kind.

By the year 2000, we hope to have almost every native UK plant species safely stored in the Millennium Seed Bank, Kew – a specially designed facility at Wakehurst Place in West Sussex. By 2010, we aim to have conserved living seeds from 10% of all plant species for the benefit of future generations.

Initially, attention will be focused on plants growing in arid areas like Africa, India and Latin America. These are the species most at risk – those on which a quarter of the world's human population depends.

Once in the Seed Bank, species can be kept for centuries or even millennia. They can be studied to discover their hidden potential, and reintroduced into the wild at any time.

One of the options given in the appeal leaflet (but not shown in the extract) for people who would like to help, is to leave a legacy. Elsewhere the reader is told that the names of benefactors recorded in the Millennium Seed Book will be, 'on permanent display in the Seed Bank for posterity'. This reflects an awareness (noted in Section 4.2) that most people want to be remembered positively after their death.

Plants are already a major source of medicines. In 1990, sales in the USA of prescriptions where material of plant origin was the active ingredient totalled US$14 500 million. For many centuries, people around the world have relied on herbal remedies of various kinds in the prevention and cure of ailments and diseases. There are over 21 000 medicinal plants named by the World Health Organisation. Although there is some duplication where plants are known by different names in different places, there will be other plants that have not yet found their way on to this list. This is a huge resource, but the value of the majority of these plants has yet to be tested scientifically. One of the cultures where there is a great deal of written information on herbal lore is found within the Indian subcontinent. The Ayurvedic system of medicine traces its written origins back to texts known as the Vedas that were written about 4 000 years ago. Ayurveda is a way of life and not just a curative system. Its philosophy embodies an holistic approach to medicine. Diet and behaviour are given equal prominence when health issues are contemplated. The individual is viewed within the framework of society, importance being attached to the well-being of both. Thus, a need for medication is seen as an unfortunate last resort. The theoretical grounding of Ayurvedic medicine is very like Western medicine, in that the principle of homeostasis is very much to the fore. Health is maintained through a dynamic balance of three fundamental elements, a theory that initially sounds alien to Western ears. It turns out that these elements embody the physiological processes as we understand them; they are merely categorized in a different way. Where Ayurveda differs from the Western approach to health is that it has always given the mind, soul and body equal importance. Not only must the body be in physiological balance for health, but it must also be in a healthy balance with mind and soul. The individual's physiological, psychological and religious states must all be in good health because they are inextricably linked. Strict religious codes have ensured that adequate attention is given to hygiene and diet. Within this tradition, there are around 1 000 plants that have been named and their medicinal properties described. Only now are we beginning to assess the values of these plants in a scientific way. One such study involves collaboration between the Centre for Ageing Research in India and the University of Illinois in the USA. They will clinically test Ayurvedic herbs listed in ancient literature as cures for *smritirhransh*, the Ayurvedic name for loss of memory. It is thought that this might be Alzheimer's disease, a condition that is causing much concern in India (and elsewhere). In a society that largely lacks benefits such as pensions, individuals must keep working. India has a high population growth rate (2.1% per annum). With a current (1997) population of around 950 million and a projected population of 1 680 million by 2050 there is concern about the ability to generate sufficient wealth to maintain current living standards. Alzheimer's is a neurodegenerative disease, the major symptoms of which are loss of memory and altered perception. People with Alzheimer's are not only unable to contribute to the economy, but they also need active nursing. Alzheimer's disease and the very similar senile dementias affect 15% of the population who are over 65 years of age. So the fact that humanity as a whole is ageing (Chapter 2 of this book), together with India's high population growth rate, make this a particularly urgent area of research for that country. Investigating the properties of traditional remedies has been fruitful in the past, as can be seen in Table 4.3.

Table 4.3 Some pharmaceuticals derived from plants and fungi.

Drug	Use	Plant source	Plant's native range
bromelain	controls tissue inflammation	pineapple (*Ananas comosus*)	tropical America
caffeine	stimulant, central nervous system	tea (*Camellia sinensis*)	South and East Asia
cocaine	local anaesthetic	coca (*Erythroxylon coca*)	East Andes
codeine, morphine	analgesics	opium poppy (*Papaver somniferum*)	Western Mediterranean
digitoxin	cardiac stimulant	foxgloves (*Digitalis* species)	Europe, Mediterranean
diosgenin	source of female contraceptive	wild yams (*Dioscorea* species)	tropics
L–Dopa	Parkinson's disease suppressant	velvet bean (*Mucuna deeringiana*)	tropics
gossypol	male contraceptive	cotton (*Gossypium* species)	warm temperate and topics
monocrotaline	anti-cancer (externally applied)	*Crotalaria sessiliflora*	tropics and subtropics
penicillin	general antibiotic	penicillin fungi (especially *Penicillium chrysogenum*)	
quinine	anti-malarial	yellow cinchona (*Cinchona ledgeriana*)	Andes to Costa Rica
reserpine	reduces high blood pressure	Indian snakeroot (*Rauvolfia serpentina*)	Tropics
scopolamine	sedative	thornapple (*Datura metel*)	South and North America, but widely naturalized
D-tubocurarine	active component of curare; surgical muscle relaxant	*Chondrodendron* and *Strychnos* species	Tropics
vinblastine, vincristine	anti-cancer, especially childhood leukaemia	Madagascar periwinkle (*Catharanthus roseus*)	Madagascar

In addition to the re-discovery of medicinal plants we continue to discover novel compounds from plant sources. The yew, *Taxus baccata*, has long been used to provide beautiful veneers for high-quality furniture but country people are wary of its leaves because they are extremely poisonous to all livestock. Who would have thought that in the 1990s these same leaves would be used to extract taxol, a powerful new drug used in the treatment of breast and ovarian cancer? What other useful substances lie waiting for us in the familiar plants of the countryside?

The reasons for wishing to preserve **biodiversity** (species and habitat diversity) are not purely pragmatic. A recent (1995) UK government steering group established the principle that

> … *we should hand on to the next generation an environment no less rich than the one we ourselves have inherited.*

To this end, costed plans were published to reverse the decline of 116 of Britain's fastest disappearing plants and animals. Part of the plan involves the protection of certain habitats such as hedgerows and coastal lagoons. Despite the fact that the World Charter for Nature, adopted by the United Nations in 1982, expressed absolute support for the principle of conserving biodiversity, the UK's plans are the first to be published by any of the countries that signed the UN convention.

Summary of Section 4.5

Human activity has been responsible for some extinctions and other deleterious changes to habitats. These changes have not always been the result of thoughtless or selfish behaviour; often intentions were worthy but outcomes were not as predicted. The importance of genetic diversity (already noted in Book 1 with reference to human populations containing individuals resistant to new infectious diseases) is demonstrated here in relation to Dutch Elm disease. The need to retain genetic diversity in plants, used for food and medicine, is recognized in such initiatives as the Kew Millennium Seed Bank Appeal.

4.6 Pollution

Unfortunately, halting the disappearance of species cannot be achieved simply by measures such as putting fences around special habitats and asking people not to pick the flowers or disturb the breeding birds. Many species are vanishing because of **pollution**. You probably have a good understanding of the meaning of this term, but it is variously defined. The Open University has a course on environmental control and public health, in which pollution is defined as the introduction into the environment (air, water, or land) of contaminants, the quantities, characteristics and duration of which are likely to be injurious to human, animal, or plant life.

Here we only have space to consider a few ways in which pollution impacts on human health. In some instances, there are clear links between health and pollution but more often, because interactions within the ecosystem are so complex, it is difficult to be certain of our ground.

4.6.1 Air pollution

There are many popular beliefs about air quality and health. As a child you might have been exhorted to, 'go out and play in the nice fresh air'. Mountain air is often regarded as being particularly beneficial, especially for those who are recuperating from or suffering some types of respiratory diseases. In Chapter 2 of Book 3, the adjustments to high altitude were discussed.

❑   Over a period of time, the body adjusts to functioning normally at low P_{O_2} (i.e. the body adapts to high altitude). Describe how these changes to the respiratory and circulatory system would benefit someone with a respiratory disease.

◼   Pulmonary ventilation increases, so more air is drawn into the lungs. Oxygen can be used more efficiently because there is an increase in the number of red blood cells and in tissue vascularization. Cardiac output is also improved as a consequence of an increase in blood volume. All of these changes improve the efficiency of the respiratory system and could counteract damage caused by disease or pollution.

The damage that can be caused by pollution has already been described (Book 3, Chapter 2). The lungs' response to polluted air can lead to the development of chronic bronchitis and ultimately emphysema, which is often now called 'smoker's lung'. But one of the fastest-growing health problems world-wide is asthma. In the popular press the cause of asthma is often said, incorrectly, to be industrial pollution. There is no scientific evidence for this causal link.

❑   How does the geographical distribution of asthma counter suggestions that it is caused by industrial pollution?

▓   The increase in asthma is world-wide.

❑   What factors are believed to trigger asthma attacks?

▓   They are thought to be triggered by allergens (Book 2, Chapter 5) and you might remember that the first occurrences of asthma recorded in the highlands of New Guinea were attributed to house dust mites brought in on imported cotton blankets (Book 3, Chapter 2).

Although acute asthma attacks appear to be precipitated by an allergic response to inhaled particles of plant or animal proteins, asthma can, like other respiratory conditions, be exacerbated by industrial air pollution.

Exact relationships between air quality and health are hard to establish, as we have to rely on epidemiological evidence rather than scientific experimentation. There is also a wide range of susceptibility between different individuals and between people of different ages. As you might expect, the very young and the very old are most at risk. There may be an immediate effect but there can also be long-term effects. There were 4 000 excess (i.e. additional) deaths attributed to the 1952 London smog (smog is a combination of smoke particles and fog droplets). Of these, 90% were persons aged 45 or older (we are not implying that members of this group are necessarily 'old'!); amongst infants of 12 months or less the death rate doubled. Some deaths occurred during the smog but others were recorded immediately afterwards. Studies suggested that the high levels of pollutants at that time had lowered the resistance of these individuals to diseases such as influenza, and their resistance remained low for a period although the air quality had improved. The pollutants implicated in this episode were smoke particles and sulphur dioxide (SO_2). Both are emissions from burning fuels; sulphur dioxide is also produced in many industrial processes. Levels of these two pollutants have been monitored in the UK since 1912. Table 4.4 shows a clear correlation between episodes of high concentrations of these substances in the atmosphere and increased mortality from respiratory disease.

Table 4.4   Some air pollution episodes in London.

Date	Pollutants (concn in micrograms per cubic metre)	Meteorology	Health effects
9–11 December 1873		fog	650 excess deaths
26–29 January 1880		fog	1 176 excess deaths
26 November –1 December 1948	smoke (200–2 800) SO$_2$ (250–2 100)	visibility, 24–400 m wind speed, 0–4.6 mph	700–800 excess deaths
5–9 December 1952	smoke (4 500) SO$_2$ (3 800)	fog visibility, 20–210 m wind speed, 0–5.8 mph	4 000 excess deaths bronchitis emphysema cardiovascular disorder wheezy chest dyspnoea fever
3–6 January 1956	smoke (to 2 400) SO$_2$ (to 1 500)		1 000 excess deaths
5–10 December 1962	smoke (> 4 000) SO$_2$ (> 4 000)		700 excess deaths

❏   In which season do all these air pollution episodes occur?

■   Winter.

❏   Why do these episodes all occur in winter?

■   The pollutants were from burning fuels. The need for heating is greatest in winter and the population density in London is high.

There are also meteorological reasons for the pollutants remaining at or near ground level rather than being dispersed into the upper atmosphere.

Whilst the need for domestic and commercial heating is highest in winter in cool climates, in warmer cities a different kind of smog is prevalent which has effects on health that are just as severe. This is exemplified by the photochemical smog in cities like San Francisco, USA. Here, the main pollutants are chemicals from traffic emissions (oxides of nitrogen and ozone) trapped close to ground level by local climatic conditions. Regulations to combat polluting emissions from vehicles now exist in economically developed countries (EDCs), such as those of the European Union (EU) and the USA. There are also Clean Air Acts in these countries. However, these acts target the *dispersal* of industrial pollutants, for example by the use of high chimneys, as much as the reduction of emissions. In the main, it is expensive to reduce emissions and this presents particular problems for economically less developed countries (ELDCs). They wish to reap the benefits of industrialization but cannot afford to use the more expensive techniques that are needed to clean up emissions. Table 4.5 compares levels of air pollution in EDCs and ELDCs recorded in the mid-1980s. Since then, conditions have generally improved in EDCs but have deteriorated in ELDCs.

Table 4.5 Air pollution levels in selected cities (micrograms per cubic metre), 1982–1985. (n.a. = data not available)

	Peak levels of particulate matter	Peak levels of SO$_2$
Economically developed countries (EDCs)		
Hamilton (Canada)	261	131
New York City (USA)	121	116
Brussels (Belgium)	97	205
Copenhagen (Denmark)	383	135
Helsinki (Finland)	516	103
Athens (Greece)	325	118
Frankfurt (Germany)	117	230
Milan (Italy)	n.a.	798
Warsaw (Poland)	248	205
London (UK)	77	171
Economically less developed countries (ELDCs)		
Rio de Janeiro (Brazil)	230	383
Sao Paulo (Brazil)	338	173
Santiago (Chile)	402	188
Beijing (China)	1 307	625
Shanghai (China)	738	217
Bombay (India)	468	85
Calcutta (India)	1 062	197
Jakarta (Indonesia)	551	197
Tehran (Iran)	701	467
Manila (Philippines)	579	198
Bangkok (Thailand)	741	48

Air pollution problems in ELDCs are of concern, not for altruistic reasons, but because air does not acknowledge national borders. Pollutants generated in one country can, in time, affect many other countries. As an illustration, between 27 November and 5 December 1962, there were high levels of air pollution noted in a number of major cities in the north of the USA. Similar conditions hit London on 5 December (Table 4.4), nine days after they had first been noted in New York; two days later they were reported from Germany, then France, Czechoslovakia and Holland in Europe; later still Osaka in Japan was affected too.

Sulphur dioxide and oxides of nitrogen have direct effects on health, particularly on the health of those people who have respiratory diseases (Book 3, Chapter 2). There is an indirect effect too because they are responsible for the deposition of acid rain which damages many organisms, and potentially this could include humans, through the workings of food webs. The increased acidity of aquatic environments encourages the uptake of toxic ions of the so-called *heavy metals* – lead, mercury, cadmium, copper and nickel – by the primary consumers.

❏   What are the primary consumers in this ecosystem?

■   The vegetation found in rivers, lakes and ponds (algae and pond
       weeds). The mass of water in oceans and seas is so large that the
       effects of acid rain are diluted to an indiscernible level.

The result so far seems to have been a depletion of fish stocks as adults are
poisoned and eggs fail to develop. No cases of human poisoning following
the ingestion of contaminated fish have been reported as a consequence of
acid rain, but this remains a possibility. Establishing that acid rain is a
global problem and getting international agreements on air quality has
taken decades. There is still no scientific agreement on the extent to which
acid rain causes certain types of environmental damage, but other concerns,
such as the depletion of the ozone layer in the upper atmosphere and global
warming, are forcing the international community to collectively examine
issues surrounding air pollution. Some of the difficulties can be illustrated
in relation to the phenomenon of global warming.

4.6.2 Global warming

Media attention has been such that it would be hard to have missed the fact
that global warming is considered to be a 'bad thing'. Why should this be
so? What is so wrong with being a bit warmer? Anyway, is global warming
really occurring and, if it is, what are the causal factors responsible for it?

Let us deal with this last question first. As we sit on a beach in summer, or
in a sunny window seat in winter, we are aware of the Earth being warmed
by the Sun. In fact the Earth is warmer than would be expected from the
amount of solar radiation that it receives, because heat is trapped by various
gases in the atmosphere. Provided that the solar radiation remains constant
and the composition of the atmosphere is unaltered, these so-called
'greenhouse gases' maintain a surface temperature hospitable to life on
Earth. But it is being suggested that the composition of the atmosphere is
altering, and that this is leading to global warming. How can we find out if
this is the case?

In the 1950s the physicist Charles Keeling developed the instrumentation
to measure atmospheric carbon dioxide, one of the most important of the
greenhouse gases. Since then continuous records have been kept by the
Mauna Loa Climate Observatory in Hawaii. A portion of that record is
reproduced as Figure 4.7, which shows a regular pattern of fluctuations in
carbon dioxide concentration.

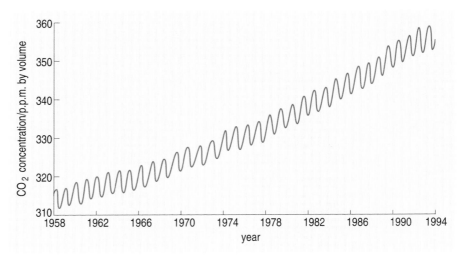

Figure 4.7 Concentration, in parts per million by volume, of atmospheric carbon dioxide measured at the Mauna Loa Climate Observatory, Hawaii. This observatory is geographically remote from any sources of pollution.

❏   How often do peaks occur? (*Hint*: You will find it easier to work this out if you take a small chunk of the graph, say from 1962–1966, and count the number of peaks over that time period.)

■   Between 1962 and 1966 there are four peaks, evenly spaced. This means that peaks occur annually.

The peaks occur in the Northern Hemisphere spring. In other words, during spring the amount of carbon dioxide in the atmosphere starts to fall.

❏   Figure 4.8 shows the ways in which carbon dioxide enters and leaves the atmosphere. Use this to list the ways in which carbon dioxide leaves the atmosphere, and then decide what might be responsible for the drop in atmospheric carbon dioxide over the spring and summer period.

■   1   Carbon dioxide passes from the atmosphere into the oceans.
    2   Carbon dioxide is taken up by plants for photosynthesis.

    In spring and summer, plants grow more vigorously than they do in autumn and winter. Thus their rate of photosynthesis increases and so more carbon dioxide is taken from the atmosphere. Consequently, this biological activity is likely to be responsible for the drop in atmospheric carbon dioxide over the spring and summer period.

You might have wondered whether oceans hold more carbon dioxide as their temperature rises. If you have noticed that 'fizzy' drinks are described as being 'carbonated' then you will know the answer! They don't! Warm, fizzy drinks gush out of their containers once opened; the 'fizz' is bubbles of carbon dioxide. In spring and summer, the oceans warm slightly and thus hold marginally less carbon dioxide than they do in winter. This would tend to counteract the effect of increased photosynthesis, making the annual fluctuations less dramatic.

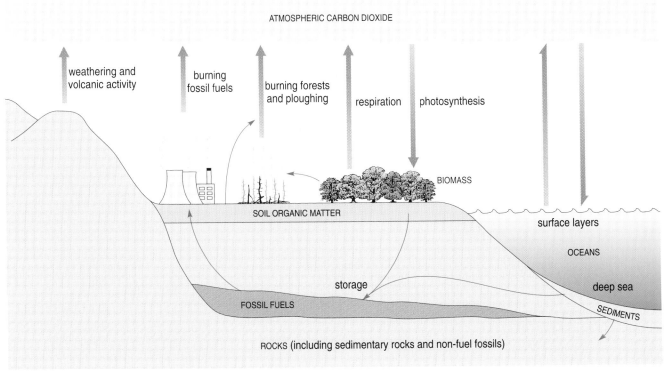

Figure 4.8   The complete carbon cycle. Note the carbon dioxide inputs to the atmosphere from human activities.

❑   Look again at Figure 4.7, at the 30-year period from 1958–1988. Does this show an increase, decrease or no change in the amount of carbon dioxide in the atmosphere?

■   Over the 30-year period there has been an increase in the amount of carbon dioxide in the atmosphere.

In fact, the average annual concentration was 315 parts per million (p.p.m.) in 1958 and had risen to 350 p.p.m. by 1988. (Expressing these concentrations in p.p.m. is just a bit neater than saying that the composition of the atmosphere has changed from 0.0315% to 0.0350% carbon dioxide.)

❑   What is the percentage increase in atmospheric carbon dioxide concentration betwen 1958 and 1988?

■   The increase was by 35 p.p.m., which is $\frac{35}{315} \times 100 = 11\%$.

Having seen that there is an annual fluctuation in the concentration of carbon dioxide in the atmosphere, it is reasonable to ask whether the recent rise in atmospheric carbon dioxide levels is part of a longer-term pattern or cycle of fluctuations. In order to answer this question, we would need to find ways of estimating *past* levels of atmospheric carbon dioxide. Somewhat surprisingly, it is possible to do this. An historical record of atmospheric composition can be found in polar ice. As snow is added to ice sheets, air is trapped in pores and isolated from the atmosphere. In this way samples of the Earth's atmosphere have been preserved in frozen layers.

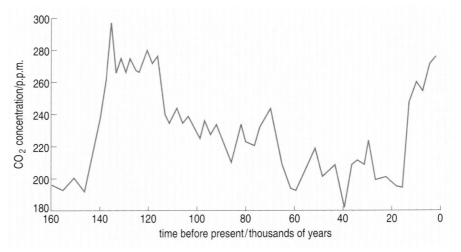

Figure 4.9   Carbon dioxide concentrations, in parts per million (p.p.m.) by volume, in the Vostock ice core over the past 160 000 years.

Figure 4.9 shows atmospheric carbon dioxide concentration for the past 1601000 years calculated from samples of a core of ice over two kilometres (km) deep, taken from Vostock, Antarctica. (Imagine the equipment you need to extract ice from that depth without damage!) The information is not very precise, because ice pores undoubtedly remained in contact with the atmosphere for variable amounts of time, probably between 10 and 11000 years, after snowfall. In addition, the age of the piece of core being analysed has to be determined by *estimating* ice flow mechanisms and the rate of ice accumulation. Nevertheless, we can see that atmospheric carbon dioxide concentration has twice risen from about 190 p.p.m. to around 280 p.p.m.

❏   What percentage increase does this represent?

■   The increase was by 90 p.p.m., which is $\frac{90}{190} \times 100 = 47\%$.

❏   Over what time period has this change taken place (approximately)?

■   10 000 years.

So, as can be seen from Figure 4.9, there have been marked fluctuations in levels of atmospheric carbon dioxide in the past.

❏   Do you think the current increase in atmospheric carbon dioxide levels is part of this natural variation? (*Hint*: Compare the results from your last two calculations.)

■   If you think not, you are in agreement with most climatologists. The changes in the chemical composition of the atmosphere seem to be taking place far more rapidly today. (An increase of 11% in carbon dioxide concentration over the past 30 years, compared to a 47% increase over about 10 000 years.)

In fact, using other ice core data shown in Figure 4.10, we believe that this accelerating increase in levels of atmospheric carbon dioxide started around the time of the first industrial activities some 200 years ago.

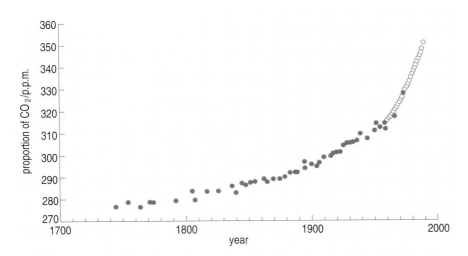

Figure 4.10   Increases in the concentration of carbon dioxide in the atmosphere over the past 250 years (black circles, estimated from ice core data; white circles, measured directly).

❑   Use Figure 4.8 to suggest the human activities that have led to an increased release of carbon dioxide into the atmosphere.

◼︎   Burning fossil fuels, burning forests and ploughing.

When the annual global output of carbon dioxide from the burning of fossil fuels is calculated, it is discovered that only about half of it contributes to the increase in the atmosphere. Where is the 'missing half'? A small amount may be used by plants growing faster, but the majority seems to dissolve in the oceans. The ability of the oceans to be flexible in the amount they absorb depends, in the first instance, upon a relationship between the ocean's plant life (the phytoplankton) and movement of water between the warmer surface layers, where the plants must live to receive enough light for photosynthesis, and the colder layers that are rich in the nutrients that the plants need and which must, therefore, be circulated to the surface. A disturbing suggestion made in 1994, was that warming of the oceans could lead to reduced mixing of these layers and hence reduced growth of phytoplankton.

❑   What effect would this have on the numbers of animal plankton (zooplankton)?

◼︎   The numbers would decrease because the phytoplankton are their food source.

In 1995, a report from Dean Roemmich and John McGowan of the Scripps Institute of Oceanography noted an 80% decrease in zooplankton since 1951, together with a 1.5 °C increase in ocean surface temperatures in the Pacific Ocean off the coast of California. It seems that the ocean's ability to absorb carbon dioxide may already be compromised.

❑   Suggest another reason to be concerned about the decrease in zooplankton numbers.

◼︎   Through the workings of food webs there will be a knock-on effect on the productivity of the oceans.

Table 4.1 showed that the NPP of oceans is quite low. However, the oceans cover 70% of the Earth's surface and fishing is vital for the economy of some people.

In this short section we have looked at the stability of the carbon dioxide content of the atmosphere and seen that fluctuations occur naturally. The subtleties of the control of the levels of atmospheric carbon dioxide are clearly very complex and a long way from being fully understood. We need to know how much more carbon dioxide can enter the atmosphere before triggering catastrophic climate change. The only hope of reaching an understanding is if scientists from different disciplines continue to work together on programmes such as the *International Geosphere–Biosphere Programme* (*IGBP*) established in 1986 and described by the *Intergovernmental Panel on Climate Change* (*IPCC*) as

> *… an inter-disciplinary research initiative … to understand the interactive physical, chemical and biological processes that regulate the total Earth system, … including those which control the concentration of carbon dioxide and other chemicals in the atmosphere.*

By the mid-1990s it became clear that, whilst we cannot make accurate predictions of how far or how fast global warming is proceeding, climatic change is definitely occurring and is brought about by human activities. Furthermore, the predicted effects on human health are universally negative. They range from fairly direct effects such as the increase in the number of deaths from cardiovascular problems which occurs during heat waves, particularly when the temperature soars above 30 °C, to the loss of life, homes and agricultural land that would result from flooding when the ocean levels rise.

To some extent, loss of life in very hot spells would be offset by fewer deaths in very cold spells. There is the possibility of adapting behaviour to cope with climatic change, particularly for those people who live in the EDCs. Routines could be changed to reduce the likelihood of overheating, and homes and offices could be air-conditioned. This assumes that the major climatic problem associated with global warming will be increased temperatures. There are models which predict that global warming will bring more episodes of violent weather changes such as hurricanes and prolonged monsoon seasons. This would wreak havoc over short timespans and it might not be possible to evacuate people, particularly from densely inhabited areas in ELDCs. As a result, there could be widespread loss of life followed by epidemics of the kinds of diseases that flourish when urban infrastructures collapse such as cholera. A similar scenario could be brought about by a different mechanism, namely as a result of flooding following a rise in the ocean level caused by a combination of thermal expansion of water and melting of polar ice. Some of the world's most densely populated areas and most productive farmlands lie along the coasts and rivers that would be the first to be affected by any such rises. In this latter scenario, there are even longer-term effects as productive land remained submerged, perhaps lost for ever. Food shortages would be added to the difficulties faced by the displaced populations. Although a climatic shift would make huge tracts of land in Canada and Siberia suitable for grain production, there are concerns that the soils would not be sufficiently fertile to sustain the high levels of production currently achieved in North America and in the wheatlands of Europe.

There are a number of diseases which would move into areas that are currently affluent and densely populated. In this context, we mean those requiring another species as host for part of their life cycle. The best-known is probably malaria where the infective agent, *Plasmodium* (a single-celled organism), requires the female *Anopheles* mosquito to complete its life cycle. But there are a number of other mosquito-borne diseases that could spread into temperate latitudes should these areas become warmer. These include yellow fever, Rift Valley fever, dengue fever and arbovirus encephalitides. They could cause considerable damage in populations unprepared for their arrival before any (costly) preventative health measures were taken.

Many scientists regard pollution as the greatest hazard threatening the continuation of any kind of life, let alone healthy life on this planet, and global warming as a kind of unstoppable time-bomb. Of all the greenhouse gases, carbon dioxide is the most troublesome because of the sheer scale of its production and the amount of time that it remains in the atmosphere. It is estimated that just to stabilize current levels would require an immediate drop of 60% in emissions. This is unlikely to happen whilst ELDCs are increasing industrialization, and in the EDCs neither the USA nor the UK have been prepared to offer more than a resolve to hold emissions at current levels.

4.6.3 The ozone hole

Another group of greenhouse gases, the chlorofluorocarbons (CFCs), are double villains because they are also implicated in the destruction of the ozone in the upper atmosphere. CFCs are synthetic gases used in aerosols, as solvents and as coolants in refrigerators. They are also used to make a light insulating material called Styrofoam, from which packaging for hot take-away food containers can be constructed. It has been easier to get international cooperation to ban further production of CFCs and you might be able to hazard a guess as to why this should be so.

❏   Why would it be easier to stop the release of CFCs into the atmosphere than to prevent further emissions of carbon dioxide?

■   We can find other substances to take over the function of CFCs. We do not depend upon them in the way that we depend upon combustion to release various types of energy.

Production of CFCs should eventually cease altogether, thanks to universal consensus concerning their deleterious effects on the environment. An international agreement aimed at achieving this (known as the Montreal Protocol), was signed by most of the industrial nations in 1987. Unfortunately, CFCs are stable compounds and only decompose slowly, so they will contribute to global warming for some time, especially as each CFC molecule has the same effect as about 20 000 molecules of carbon dioxide. As CFCs decay, they release chlorine and it is this gas that leads to the breakdown of the ozone layer. Ozone in the upper atmosphere helps to shield plant and animal life from dangerous ultraviolet (uv) radiation. Since the thinning of the ozone layer was first noticed, there has been an increase in the reported incidence of of skin cancers. There is another part of our bodies that is particularly susceptible to damage from uv radiation (mentioned in Chapter 2 of this book).

❑   Name the organ that is easily damaged by sunlight.

◼   The eye.

So you won't be surprised to learn that the increased incidence in cataracts is attributed to increased exposure to uv radiation. Finally, it should be mentioned that laboratory studies indicate that the effectiveness of the immune system is compromised by uv radiation.

4.6.4 Indoor pollutants

Before leaving air pollution you might reflect that many of us spend most of our time indoors where the air quality can differ from that outside the building.

❑   In what ways will the air be different inside a building?

◼   The air is sometimes described as stale. Usually this just means that it is warm, but it can also mean that there are odours from bodies and a slightly elevated carbon dioxide content from people exhaling. If there are smokers, there will be tobacco fumes too. A condition called 'sick building syndrome' has also been described.

'Sick' buildings suffer from air pollution of a particular kind. Ozone formed at ground level from traffic emissions can react with materials in furnishings, such as carpets, to produce toxic fumes of chemicals (for example formaldehyde and benzene) which are tissue irritants. These give rise to symptoms of nausea, headaches and dizziness. They also exacerbate any respiratory disorders.

The same is true of tobacco smoke as it too contains formaldehyde. Eyes and throats tend to be most irritated by tobacco smoke. A great deal has been written about passive smoking so you'll probably be aware that some of these noxious tobacco fumes are carcinogenic and can damage the lungs of non-smokers too.

4.6.5 Land and water pollution

In this section we will just take a couple of examples which show how easy it is to expose ourselves to long-term damage inadvertently. Pesticides, developed to control insects and other vermin, can increase agricultural productivity. Although pesticides were originally hailed as one of the wonders of modern technology, it was quite quickly discovered that there was a downside to their widespread use. One problem was that of **bioaccumulation**. Pesticides tended to be stable chemicals and through the workings of the food chain they became concentrated in the tissues of carnivores. This was first noticed when birds like the eagle showed poor hatching success. Eggs that had failed to hatch were analysed and shown to have high levels of pesticides such as the organochloride substance dichlorodiphenyltrichloroethane (DDT). There are 129 substances (including DDT) that are so toxic that there is agreement within the EU that pollution by them must be stopped completely. Unfortunately many of them continue to be used in ELDCs. The regulations on the application and handling of pesticides hold no sway in these areas and there is evidence of a considerable level of direct poisoning. One study suggested that in parts of Indonesia about 20% of farmers observed spraying had neurological, respiratory or intestinal symptoms of poisoning (Kishi, 1995). Organophosphates are now the more widely used class of pesticides. They are far more toxic to insects than to mammals and they are broken down more rapidly, into biologically inert products, so they are classified as safer. This is very much a relative term! The organophosphates inhibit the activity of acetylcholinesterase (AChE), which is the enzyme that breaks down the neurotransmitter acetylcholine (ACh).

❏ Name a major site of ACh release.

◼ ACh is the neurotransmitter used at the neuromuscular junction. (Book 2, Chapter 4).

❏ What is its action there?

◼ It triggers muscular activity.

❏ What will be the outcome of inhibiting AChE?

◼ In the absence of AChE, the muscle remains active.

The amount of ACh will increase in quantity as each new impulse arrives at the neuromuscular junction. ACh binds to receptors at the muscle cell membrane and is then released into the synapse. In the absence of AChE, molecules of ACh will re-attach to receptors and repeatedly stimulate the muscle. This results in muscles going into spasm. Muscle spasms at the larynx will prevent air from entering the lungs and a person poisoned by organophosphates will in effect die by suffocation.

But many incidents of poisoning are sub-lethal and not seen by any health workers. The more severe cases are often misdiagnosed and assumed to be stroke, respiratory or even cardiovascular disease. We have no idea whether there will be any longer-term effects of these chemicals but there are suspicions that they are carcinogenic. There is also a range of studies that provide evidence of immunosuppression by pesticides. Unfortunately, the application of pesticides isn't very efficient. Only about 15% of the pesticide actually reaches the target pest; the rest is dispersed into the environment, especially on windy days. Amongst other organisms, fish seem to be particularly susceptible to pesticide poisoning. Fish are a significant part of many human diets and high levels of pesticides are found in individuals who live in areas far removed from those where the pesticides were used.

DDT exhibits another unfortunate characteristic (which it shares with a range of unrelated chemicals) in that it mimics the effects of oestrogen.

❏   What kind of substance is oestrogen?

■   Oestrogen is a steroid and also a sex hormone (Book 1, Chapter 3).

When DDT or other oestrogen agonists bind to oestrogen receptors they will inappropriately initiate activity in several quite different tissues. In general this activity relates to reproductive events. For example, overactivity of oestrogen receptors will have a feminizing effect on males. This might explain why there have been reports of human sperm counts falling in recent years, the outcome of which could be lower fertility. Oestrogen is also required for successful implantation, as mentioned in Book 1, Chapter 6. A widespread class of organic pollutants, the polychlorinated biphenyls (PCBs), are also oestrogen mimics, and there is evidence of animals with high tissue concentrations of PCBs showing abnormal reproductive behaviour, reduced fertility and defective reproductive systems (Colborn, Dumanoski and Myers, 1996). Whilst the evidence for interference with human reproduction is as yet scant, the outlook is not very encouraging. Concern has been expressed that the habit of covering food in cling film and microwaving food in plastic containers increases our exposure to PCBs and thereby the possibility of their contaminating our foodstuffs and being ingested.

These are two examples of materials designed to make life more hygienic that seem instead to pose serious threats to our well-being. It is very hard when developing new technologies and new materials to be sure where they are leading us. This is true in another sense, for the more successful we are in promoting health and longevity, the closer we come to provoking a different kind of catastrophe, that of over-population.

Summary of Section 4.6

Pollution damages organisms, including ourselves. The link between air pollution and health is hard to quantify. It has to be extrapolated from epidemiological studies and is complicated because susceptibilities vary. Many pollutants are produced by industrial processes and it is expensive to reduce their emission into the environment. There are also difficulties in predicting the long-term effects on climate of airborne pollutants such as CFCs and carbon dioxide. These scientific uncertainties, together with the financial constraints, make it difficult to obtain international cooperation to reduce emissions. Not all pollutants are byproducts of industry; some, such as pesticides and certain plastics, were developed to improve the quality of life.

4.7 Population growth

It has already been stated (Section 4.2) that three factors check population growth. These are predation, disease and insufficient food supply. For much of our history, our ancestors' numbers were indeed limited by wars, disease and famine. The world population remained relatively stable until around 300 years ago. Then at the begining of the 19th century (100 years after population growth started its geometric increase), the demographer Thomas Malthus predicted that population growth would outstrip food production and would then crash, the crash being brought about by any catastrophic event such as famine, war or disease. So far, agricultural productivity has exceeded everyone's expectations and famines have been the result of shortfalls in particular regions, coupled with an inability or a lack of will to redistribute excess production from other areas. Also, in many ELDCs population growth rates have fallen, but this is largely because infant mortality has remained high. Therefore the primary health-care needs of ELDCs are still seen as crucial to curbing population increase. Parents continue to produce more children than they really want but a proportion will almost certainly not survive beyond infancy. A better-educated population is more able to make health choices, choosing contraception and learning simple techniques to combat disease, such as oral rehydration.

Some of the consequences of increasing populations have been unexpected, such as environmental damage and accidents resulting from inadequate safety measures as ELDCs strive to increase their output and wealth through industrialization. These have posed at least as great a threat as poor agricultural practices; the latter are leading to loss of agricultural land through soil erosion, desertification and increasing soil salinity.

Meantime, population growth in Africa continues at 3% per annum and there is not enough food or clean water to sustain this level of growth. So, although there may theoretically be enough food grown world-wide to feed everyone, we will continue to hear of famine and undernourished communities in ELDCs.

4.8 Some philosophical issues

We began this course by trying to give you a framework in which to make sense of your studies; we wanted you to understand what we hoped could be achieved by studying SK220. So it seems reasonable to end by asking you to take a little time to reflect on what you have got out of the course. In this final chapter we have considered global issues that have implications for our health and the health of future generations. This places our own lives in a different context and also indicates the uncertainties that surround the future. Whilst some environmental changes have very direct health consequences, we should not forget the *indirect* benefits that accrue from a healthy planet. The principle that 'we should hand on to the next generation an environment no less rich than the one we ourselves have inherited', echoes the stewardship philosophy that first emerged in Britain amongst intellectuals such as Samuel Taylor Coleridge. In the ballad, 'The Rime of the Ancient Mariner', Coleridge (1798) develops the theme of the horrible consequences for one individual (the mariner) of wantonly killing an albatross. Through this act he brings about the death of fellow sailors. From other writings it is clear that Coleridge deplored cruelty and believed that the lives of all living things should be respected or there would be dire consequences for humanity. This view contrasted with the contemporary view (of the Western world) that humans were apart from the rest of the natural world and had the right to control and use it as they wished. Coleridge's perspective was further developed in the 19th century and might be seen as the predecessor of today's conservation movement.

The extent to which the richness and beauty of the natural world affects our health and well-being has been widely debated. The debate often centres around the negative effects of environments such as inner cities that are far removed from 'wild Nature'. It is interesting to note that writings from the 17th century and earlier use words such as 'dangerous', 'hideous', 'ghastly' and 'terrible' to describe the very places in England (Pennines, Lake District) that are now sought out for rest and relaxation. You might have ideas to explain the diametrically opposed opinions of different eras about the character of the English countryside. In doing this you could well draw on the arguments of social constructionism found in Book 1, Chapter 1.

If it is felt that more direct contact with nature is therapeutic, some questions of accessibility are raised. In crowded industrial countries, the countryside is largely land that is owned by individuals who use it to generate a living (e.g. through agriculture and forestry), and public access is limited. Land that is publicly owned needs to be maintained (repairs to footpaths, provision of car parks), and this incurs costs that may be passed on to the user. It can also be expensive and time-consuming to reach these places. For much of the population, this may restrict access.

In Book 1, Chapter 2, the WHO definition of health, which recognizes individual and social responsibilities, was noted. The chapter also emphasized that the extent to which health is realized depends on how far individuals and groups are able to 'change or cope with the environment', but there was little reference to the natural environment. Parks and open spaces are found in lists of desirable features of environments that might promote health, but nothing beyond that. However, in this chapter we have identified some effects on health that arise from our interactions with the natural world. Furthermore, we have noted that these effects range from its amenity value to questions about its ability to support all the Earth's current population, or indeed any future populations. Many of the issues raised here are those where the ability of individuals to alter the behaviour of industry or society appears negligible. However, this may be deceptive, for we have seen a dramatic rise in the influence of grass roots organizations such as Greenpeace and Friends of the Earth. One of the benefits of modern communications technology is the way it enables individuals to join together as groups to influence those in power.

It has perhaps always been very obvious to you that health is about more than a functional body, but has SK220 brought a deeper insight into the extent of the interrelationships between body and environment? Will your new-found knowledge make any difference to the way in which you live your life? If you can answer 'yes' to either of these questions, we shall be more than satisfied.

Objectives for Chapter 4

After completing this chapter you should be able to:

4.1 Define and use, or recognize definitions and applications of, each of the terms printed in **bold** in the text.

4.2 Understand the complexity of the interdependence between organisms and their environment. (*Question 4.1*)

4.3 Describe some of the consequences for health of pollution. (*Question 4.2*)

4.4 Explain why it is difficult to gain international agreements to secure biodiversity and reduce pollution. (*Question 4.2*)

Questions for Chapter 4

Question 4.1   (*Objectives 4.1 and 4.2*)

Foxes eat rabbits and rabbits eat dandelions. Predict what will happen if rabbit numbers are severely reduced (e.g. by disease). How confident are you about your predictions?

Question 4.2   (*Objectives 4.3 and 4.4*)

In the UK there are some substances that it is illegal to own or use. List arguments for and against banning the sale of tobacco. Are there any reasons why a ban is unlikely?

References

Colburn, T., Dumanoski, D. and Myers, J. P. (1996) *Our Stolen Future*, Little, Brown and Co.

Kishi, M., Hirschorn, N., Djajadisastra, M., Saterlee, L. N., Strowman, S. and Dilts, R. (1995) Relationship of pesticide spraying to signs and symptoms in Indonesian farmers, *Scandinavian Journal of Work and Environmental Health*, **21** (2), pp. 124–33.

Wilson, E. O. (1992) *The Diversity of Life*, The Bellknap Press of the Harvard University Press, Cambridge, USA.

ANSWERS TO QUESTIONS

Chapter 2

Question 2.1

In old age, the cumulative effects of a life of disadvantage will take their toll on health. Women who come from a working-class background, who have had very little education and have experienced poor living conditions are the most likely to be in poor health.

Question 2.2

This would be a social or a physical difficulty. If it is a physical difficulty it could be attributed to problems with the musculo-skeletal system or vision or there might be a neurological difficulty. These physical problems might be relatively minor or anywhere along the scale to full disease status. The sort of social problems that prevent people 'getting about' include lack of money, isolation and embarrassment.

Question 2.3

If walking increases pain felt in joints, then the person may have arthritis. If movement is slow and unsteady, there may be wasting of muscle tissue. The person may be afraid to walk, knowing that they have osteoporosis and that a fall would almost inevitably result in a fracture that would not heal easily. The individual might have a neurological disease. If they walk with a drunken gait, this is likely to be an ataxia attributable to a damaged cerebellum. If they have problems initiating movement and then move slowly with a shuffling gait, it could be that there is a loss of dopaminergic neurons from the substantia nigra and they have Parkinson's disease.

Question 2.4

Ageing does not confer advantage to an individual and it also occurs after reproductive activity has started. Natural selection works by favouring the better-adapted individuals at the expense of the less well-adapted individuals. So, an aged individual is at a disadvantage when compared to a younger individual. However, ageing is not eliminated by natural selection because the aged individual has already left offspring (who will themselves age).

Question 2.5

The choice is yours, but here are our comments on the likelihood of each of the five products having the effects that are claimed:

1   Not likely to work! It has to prevent (or undo) cross-linking of collagen fibres, increase the water content of connective tissue and increase the subcutaneous fat layer.

2   Sounds promising! This might reduce damage by free radicals. But will the anti-oxidant be assimilated? If not, how will it get to where it is needed most? It needs to be distributed by the circulatory system, and hence be available to all cells.

3   With exams looming, you might go for this in desperation! Research on OU students has shown that older students can recall information just as well as younger students, so whatever your age don't despair! Although our brains lose cells as they age, there is spare capacity and so there does not need to be any loss of function. If there was a substance known to aid memory with no adverse side-effects, it would surely be widely publicized. There would also be the difficulty of targeting the appropriate area in the brain.

4   Would you stick to such a diet when the goal is so long-term? Latest findings suggest that a reduction of calorific intake to achieve a body weight between 10–25% less than the weight your body is 'programmed' to maintain could be beneficial in increasing lifespan. This kind of diet is so severe that it needs medical guidance.

5   So called 'stiff joints' are usually ones where cartilage has worn and where it is pain that inhibits movement. The ointment might contain an analgesic (pain-killer) but it is hard to envisage any compound that could pass through the skin, into the joint, and repair worn cartilage.

Question 2.6

The health of someone who has good social support networks will benefit directly from having the love, affection and practical help of other people. She/he will also benefit from the sense of security that comes with knowing that there are others on whom to call. Old people who have learnt to cope well with adverse life events in the past will feel more confident about facing future adversity. Education has been identified as an important factor in enabling people to acquire good coping strategies.

Chapter 3

Question 3.1

With the increased professionalization and medicalization of health during the 20th century, people with serious illnesses have been encouraged by the prospect of a cure offered by hospitals. In addition to this, the traditional carer – the wife, daughter or sister – now participates more fully in the workforce and the extended family has shrunk to the extent that many people live in very small family units without the possibility of having numerous carers available. As people live much longer, many people live on their own (their partner having predeceased them) and hence they have no family carers whatsoever.

Question 3.2

Prior to the development of hospice ideology and palliative care practice, from the end of World War I till the late 1960s, most people in the UK died in hospitals where they were sometimes neglected, deceived (about their prognosis) and their pain was not adequately controlled. With the introduction of a scientific approach to pain relief and an acknowledgement that symptoms may be caused by other pharmacological agents and also non-physical factors (emotional, spiritual, psychological), it is now recognized that dying people require specialist care. The hospice movement spearheaded the speciality of palliative care, and most areas and district general hospitals now have access to specialist nurses and physicians who can advise on the different aspects of total pain.

Question 3.3

A sluggish circulation can result in local areas of tissue having a poor blood flow through them. This means that the rate of removal of carbon dioxide is reduced. Thus the concentration of carbonic acid will increase, resulting in a rise in hydrogen ion concentration (in other words, the chemical equation shown on page 76 moves to the right). Additionally, a reduced supply of oxygen to these cells can result in the production of lactate because glycolysis has to proceed anaerobically (Book 3, Chapter 4). Both these processes contribute to increased acidity (reduced pH) of the blood.

Question 3.4

Before the Tony Bland case, there was no possibility of lawfully removing sustenance to people defined as being in a persistent vegetative state. This ruling by the Law Lords was particularly important because it recognized that feeding someone could be seen as medical treatment in much the same way as artificial ventilation.

Question 3.5

On the one hand, there are the norms of society to consider, for example, a person who dies in Japan is likely to be cremated rather than buried and a muslim dying in Britain will have to be buried in a coffin rather than a shroud. Within any society, the treatment of the body immediately following death is likely to depend on whether death occurs at home, in a hospital or in a public place (on the street or in a shop, for example). If the death occurred at home, the rituals appropriate to that persons religious and cultural affiliations would be carried out. In Britain, an unexpected death necessitates a post-mortem. This may delay release of the body. In these circumstances, some of the rituals prescribed by individual religions may not be carried out; for example, it would not be possible for a Jew to be buried within two days of death.

Question 3.6

For some people, grieving is a life-long activity and they are never able to readjust to 'normal' life without the deceased. For them, Worden's tasks of mourning are simply a prescriptive mould into which they cannot fit. They may continue to grieve openly or silently for the rest of their lives and find this quite natural. Stages of mourning are also found amongst certain religious traditions, e.g. Judaism and Islam, where grieving is supposed to fit a particular pattern with the focus on re-integration into society of the deceased person. Again this may be an unwelcome constraint for someone who feels that their grieving will never cease.

Chapter 4

Question 4.1

A simple prediction is that dandelions will flourish and the number of foxes will decline. The reduction in fox numbers in relation to rabbit numbers might resemble the predator–prey relationship shown in Figure 4.4. You should not be very confident of this prediction because it is rare for simple food chains to operate in isolation (feeding relationships between organisms are more realistically represented as food webs (e.g. Figure 4.2). In fact, when rabbit numbers were reduced by myxomatosis in the UK during the 1950s, the number of foxes did not decline but owl numbers did. This is because foxes can eat a varied diet, including insects, fruit and berries and also voles, and voles are the owl's main food source.

Question 4.2

Arguments for a ban:

1 The smoke from tobacco contains pollutants that are causally implicated as cancer-causing agents (carcinogens).

2 Smoking increases risk of cardiovascular disease (Book 3, Chapter 4).

3 The particulate matter in smoke can cause respiratory disorders such as bronchitis and emphysema (Book 3, Chapter 2).

4 Tobacco smoke in an enclosed atmosphere affects the respiratory tract of non-smokers too.

5 Babies born to mothers who smoke during pregnancy are smaller and more susceptible to disease than normal. Also the risk of miscarriage is much higher for smokers than non-smokers (Book 1, Chapter 6).

Arguments against a ban:

1 Claims made about the adverse effects of tobacco smoke on human health are based on epidemiological studies, not on evidence gained from direct experimentation on humans.

2 Individuals have the right to make their own health choices.

3 There is the possibility that *useful* substances might be obtained from the tobacco plant; a *total* ban on tobacco sales would therefore be undesirable.

The revenue from the tax on tobacco and also the considerable individual fortunes that rest on the tobacco industry might make a ban on all sales unlikely. From general knowledge you probably realize that the financial, social and scientific issues that relate to the use of tobacco are very complex.

ACKNOWLEDGEMENTS

We are grateful to Jean MacQueen who prepared the index for this book. We would also like to thank Alison Sharples, of Swallowfield Lower School, Woburn Sands, Bucks., for her help in selecting illustrations used in Chapter 3.

Grateful acknowledgement is made to the following sources for permission to reproduce material in this book:

Covers

Front and *back*: Copyright © 1995 Comstock Inc.

Figures

Figure 2.1: Courtesy of Ian Worpole/*Scientific American* 1993; *Figure 2.2*: reprinted by permission of Sage Publications Ltd from Briggs, R. (1993) 'Biological Ageing', Figure 3.2 in Bond, J., Coleman, P. and Peace, S., *Ageing in Society*, copyright © 1993 Roger Briggs, Sage Publications Ltd; *Figure 2.4*: Sidell, M. (1994) *Health in Old Age: Myth, Mystery and Management*, Figures 3.7 and 3.8, Open University Press; *Figure 2.5*: Photographic Unit, Department of Histopathology, John Radcliffe Hospital, Oxford; *Figure 2.6*: adapted from Strehler, B. L., Mark, D. D., Milchran, A. S. and Gee, M. V. (1959) 'Rate and magnitude of age pigment accumulation in the human myocardium', *Journal of Gerontology*, **14**, Figure 2, p. 434, The Gerontological Society of America; *Figure 2.8*: *Scientific American*, December 1992, © Drs Fisher, C. L., Pique, M. E. and Getzoff, E. D., Scripps Research Institute; *Figures 2.9, 2.11 and 2.13*: copyright © Sheila Dunleavy; *Figure 2.14:* copyright © Elizabeth Murray; *Figure 3.1*: courtesy of the British Museum; *Figures 3.3 and 3.11*: courtesy of Ancient Art and Architecture; *Figure 3.5*: Carola, R., Harley, J. P. and Noback, C. R. (1990) *Human Anatomy and Physiology (international edn), w*ith permission of The McGraw-Hill Companies; *Figure 3.7*: Passmore, R. and Robson, J. S. (1980) *A Companion to Medical Studies, Volume 2,*

Pharmacology, Microbiology, General Pathology and Related Subjects, 2nd edn, Blackwell Science Ltd; Figure 3.9: Press Association; *Figure 3.10*: Parkes, C. M. (1986) *Bereavement: Studies of grief in adult life*, 1996 edn, Routledge; *Figure 4.4*: after MacLulick (1937) University of Toronto studies, Biology series, **43**, pp. 1–36; *Figure 4.5*: reprinted from Pearce, T. R. (1962) *Pathology of Trees and Shrubs*, p. 419, Oxford University Press, by permission of Oxford University Press; *Figure 4.6: Millennium Seed Bank Appeal*, Royal Botanical Gardens, Kew; *Figure 4.9*: reprinted with permission from *Nature*, **329**, p. 410, Barnola, J. M., Raynaud, D., Korotkevich, Y. S. and Corious, C. (1987) 'Vostock ice core provides 160 000 year record of atmospheric CO_2', copyright © 1987 Macmillan Magazines Ltd.

Tables

Table 2.1: Sidell, M. (1994) *Health in Old Age: Myth, Mystery and Management*, Table 3.5, Open University Press; *Table 3.2*: Guyton, A. C. (1991) *Textbook of Medical Physiology*, W. B. Saunders & Company Ltd; *Table 3.3*: Parkes, C. M. (1986) *Bereavement: Studies of grief in adult life*, 1996 edn, Routledge.

Boxes

Box 3.1: Advance Directive, Voluntary Euthanasia Society; *Box 4.1: Millennium Seed Bank Appeal*, Royal Botanical Gardens, Kew.

INDEX

Note: Entries in **bold** are key terms. Page numbers in *italics* refer to figures and tables.